Best Courses in Ireland

Best Courses in
IRELAND

AURUM PRESS

First published in Great Britain 2000
by Aurum Press Ltd, 25 Bedford Avenue, London WC1B 3AT

A catalogue record for this book is available from the British Library.

ISBN 1 85410 684 8

1 3 5 7 9 10 8 6 4 2
2000 2002 2004 2003 2001

Text compiled and written by Jim Humberstone and Bill Robertson
Design by Don Macpherson
Typeset by Action Publishing Technology Ltd, Gloucester
Printed and bound by in Great Britain by
CPD Group, Wales

Contents

Foreword by Bill Robertson   vii

Preface by Steve Prentice   ix

Introduction   1

Top 20 Courses   4

10 Best Value Courses   5

10 Most Difficult Courses   6

Top 10 Courses for Welcome   7

Star Ratings   8–10

Course Listings   11–104

Index   107

Foreword

With golf, as with life, one man's meat is, more often than not, another man's poison — especially when it comes to defining exactly what constitutes a good golf course.

For many golfers the historic links courses are the oldest, most traditional and therefore quite obviously the best. Other players, however, will argue with equal conviction that nothing can match the quiet tranquillity and scenic beauty of playing the game on a mature and superbly manicured inland layout. Whatever your golfing preference, you are sure to be spoiled for choice by this great new book, which provides a comprehensive list of 200 recommended golf courses covering the length and breadth of Ireland. As well as all the essential information from green fees to visitor restrictions, you'll also learn about the best, and worst, holes, the speed of the greens, the depth of the rough and the type of terrain each course is laid out over. You can even discover exactly how friendly the natives are!

Many of the most famous golfing venues, both seaside and inland, are bound to be on your own 'must play' list of courses. But *Best Courses in Ireland* also includes a host of smaller hidden gems which you can now look forward to discovering — golf courses that more often than not boast outstanding and wonderfully scenic layouts, offer great value for money and always afford the golfing visitor the warmest of welcomes. And because all the courses featured have also been assessed by *Golf World* readers, you will be able to discover what your fellow amateur golfers have to say about them.

Bill Robertson

Preface

Welcome to *Golf World's Best Courses in Ireland*. For those of you who enjoy discovering new and exciting courses to play, this book offers the ultimate guide to some of the best-value golf to be found anywhere in the world. It has been created especially to provide readers with the essential information required to fully enjoy the wide diversity, outstanding quality and unique character of the golf courses which make Scotland such a popular golfing destination. Each of the 200 courses included has been individually rated by readers and members of *Golf World* staff to provide an overall golfing experience, by highlighting such things as: quality and difficulty of the courses, the clubhouse facilities, value for money and the friendliness – or otherwise – of the welcome you can expect. In this book we have deliberately made judgements about the courses included, to provide considerably more about the golf clubs you may consider visiting than simply the green fee, the par of the course, the address and the secretary's phone number.

Golf World's 1000 Best Golf Courses in Britain and Ireland, which was published in 1999, has already proved to be an outstanding success. This new book expands and refines this winning formula by providing the same detailed information, along with personal comments, on 200 Irish golf courses. Some of the courses are better than others. There are those which are less challenging but outstandingly scenic, while others provide as tough and demanding a test as you will find anywhere the game of golf is played. But the one thing all the 200 courses featured have in common is the fact that they have each been subjected to *Golf World's* detailed evaluation.

Whether you intend to visit the Irish courses featured with a couple of regular playing partners from your local golf club, or as a member of a larger, more organised golf society, this book will help you make the right choice. To enable you to plan your visit more easily, the book has been divided into Ireland's recognised golfing regions. Separate listings have also been given to highlight the most friendly and best value clubs, and for each region we also spotlight our favourite course, or courses. If you are the kind of golfer who enjoys the scenery as much as the golfing challenge, or if you are a committed player keen to test your skills against the very best Ireland has to offer, we trust you will find everything you are looking for in this new *Golf World* book.

Steve Prentice
Editor, *Golf World*

Introduction

Golf World launched its first nationwide survey of Irish golf courses in October 1999. Through our readers, we aimed to produce the first independent, authoritative guide to the best golf courses to play. The rankings and ratings contained in this book completely reflect the thoughts and experiences of ordinary golfers.

Lists of the best places to play are typically selected by professionals, course designers and figures of authority within the golfing industry. Unlike the golfing cognoscenti, who are not out there playing courses day in, day out, the green-fee-paying golfer is, and is often better placed to identify the strengths and weaknesses of the top courses.

Upon this premise, we asked our readers to evaluate 200 pre-selected courses in four different categories: value for money, course difficulty, quality of welcome and overall rating.

By ranking the courses in these categories, we aimed to answer questions that the typical golfer might ask before visiting a new course. Is it worth the money? Is the course too hard for a player of my standard? Where will I be made welcome? We also wanted to know what, in the opinion of the grass-roots golfers, were the best courses in Ireland.

While the ratings and rankings achieved the purpose of grading each course, we also wanted golfers' comments about them. At the foot of each entry in this guide you will find individual comments about the 200 courses from the people who have played them – in many cases the comments are as illuminating as the ratings.

Any guide that attempts to grade courses is open to criticism. People like different courses for different reasons. We are acutely aware of this fact and have tried to balance the ratings and comments to achieve a fair, rational view. Hopefully you will agree. If not, it should cause a lively debate in the club bar, and we welcome any views or comments you should have about this guide.

How to use this guide

This book has been divided into three sections for quick and easy reference. In the first section you will find the following rankings: the Top 20 Courses, the 10 Best Value Courses, the 10 Most Difficult Courses and the Top 10 Courses for Welcome.

In the second section are the star ratings for all 200 courses, rated from five star to one star as follows:

★★★★★ — Exceptional. The best.
★★★★ — Excellent. An outstanding day's golf.
★★★ — Very good.
★★ — Good, but not great.
★ — Standard – nothing special.

The third section is the main part of the book, listing all 200 Irish courses featured. Here you will find all the information you need to organise a game. The listing covers each of the Irish regions, and a review of *Golf World*'s favourite course (or courses) in the region appears at the beginning of each regional listing.

This is a typical entry:

Dingle Golf Club   ★★★★

Ballyoughheragh, Tralee, County Kerry
Nearest main town: Tralee

Secretary:	Mr T. O'Shea	Tel: 066 56408
		Fax: 066 56409
Professional:	Mr D. O'Connor	Tel: 066 56225

Playing: Midweek: round n/a; day £25.00. Weekend: round n/a: day £35.00.

Facilities: Bar: 11am–11pm. Food: Lunch and dinner from 10am–6pm. Bar snacks.

Comments: Magical setting overlooking Dingle Bay ... New links that's so exciting ... Wind wreaks havoc here ... Keep the ball as low as you can ... Links that simply teases you at every turn ... Evocative ... Preferred it to more prestigious courses in the area ... Very welcoming ... Very sandy and difficult ... Love this place ... A natural course with fine character.

– The information listed is accurate at the time of going to press. The bar and catering times given are expected opening times during the summer. In many cases during the winter, bar and catering times are likely to be shorter due to the early close of play.

– There are four possible green fee prices for weekday round/day and weekends round/day. Where there is no price next to an entry, it means that price is not available at the club. Although we have indicated the most recent prices quoted prior to going to press, green fees can change during the course of the year. Check with the golf club prior to your visit.

– The direct dialing code for the Republic of Ireland from the UK is 00 353 (then omit the first 0 of the local number).

Advice for Visitors

It often feels as though you need a special handshake to get into some golf courses. Clubs tend to be protective of their courses, much as a child guards his or her favourite toy. Provided you are a bona fide golfer and are clear on golf etiquette, there are just a few simple rules to smooth the way.

The majority of the courses listed in the book require visitors to contact the club in advance and some may require you to produce a handicap certificate on the day of play. That is normally sufficient. When approaching some of the more exclusive courses, it is recommended that you write a letter of introduction direct to the secretary or organise a letter of introduction from your own club secretary.

With the exception of a very few clubs, there is nothing to stop you playing the best courses in the country, provided you follow these basic introductions. If you do not have a handicap, then the best advice is to follow the normal procedures and hope for the best – you may be asked to prove your ability when you arrive at the club.

Clubs have many competition and society days during the year, so find out the best days for visitors before you go. If you turn up on the door, you may be disappointed. Also, men should remember to pack a jacket and tie as many clubs have a dress code in the bar and dining room.

Good golfing!

TOP 20 COURSES

1.   Royal County Down
2.   Royal Portrush (Dunluce)
3.   Ballybunion (Old)
4.   Mount Juliet
5.   Lahinch (Old)
6.   Portmarnock (Old)
7.   County Sligo (Rosses Point)
8.   Ballybunion (Cashen)
9.   Tralee
10. Old Head of Kinsale
11. Ballyliffin (Glashedy)
12. Killarney (Killeen)
13. Portstewart (Strand)
14. Waterville
15. Killarney (Mahoney's Point)
16. Dooks
17. County Tipperary
18. The European Club
19. Portsalon
20. Ballyliffin (Old)

10 BEST VALUE COURSES

1. Dooks
2. County Sligo (Rosses Point)
3. Tralee
4. Connemara
5. Tramore
6. Carlow
7. Westport
8. Headfort
9. Donegal
10. Belvoir Park

10 MOST DIFFICULT COURSES

1. Royal Portrush (Dunluce)
2. Royal County Down
3. Waterville
4. Portmarnock (Old)
5. Druid's Glen
6. Dooks
7. Lahinch (Old)
8. Ballyliffin (Old)
9. Castlerock
10. Portstewart

TOP 10 COURSES FOR WELCOME

1. Portstewart (Strand)
2. The European Club
3. Tralee
4. Mount Juliet
5. County Sligo
6. Fota Island
7. Glasson
8. Dooks
9. Warrenpoint
10. Massereene

STAR RATINGS

★★★★★

Ballybunion (Old)
Ballybunion (Cashen)
Ballyliffin (Glashedy)
County Sligo
Lahinch (Old)
Mount Juliet

Old Head
Portmarnock (Old)
Portmarnock Hotel and Golf Links
Royal County Down
Royal Portrush (Dunluce)
Tralee

★★★★

Adare Manor
Ballykisteen
Ballyliffin (Old)
Beaufort
Castlerock
Connemara
Cork
County Louth
County Tipperary
Dingle
Donegal
Dooks
Druid's Glen
Enniscrone
Galway
Glasson
Killarney (Killeen)

Killarney (Mahoney's Point)
Lahinch (Castle)
Portsalon
Portstewart
Rathsallagh
Rosapenna
Royal Dublin
Royal Portrush (Valley)
St Margarets
Templepatrick
The Belvoir Park
The European Club
The Island
The K Club
Tramore
Waterville
Westport

★★★

Ardglass
Athlone
Ballybofey & Stranorlar
Ballycastle
Ballyheigue Castle
Balmoral
Bangor
Bantry Bay
Black Bush

Bodenstown
Bundoran
Cairndhu
Carlow
Castletroy
Charlesland
Charleville
City of Derry
Clandeboye (Ava)

Clandeboye (Dufferin)
Courtown
Donabate
Dromoland Castle
Dun Laoghaire
Dundalk
Dungannon
Faithlegg House
Galway Bay
Headfort
Hermitage
Kenmare
Kilkenny
Killorglin
Kirkistown Castle
Lee Valley
Limerick County

Luttrellstown Castle
Malone
Massereene
Mount Temple
Nairn & Portnoo
Parknasilla
Powerscourt
Radisson Roe Park
Rosslare
Shannon
Slieve Russell
The Knock Club
Thurles
Tullamore
West Waterford
Woodbrook
Woodenbridge

★★

Ardee
Athenry
Athy
Balcarrick
Ballinasloe
Ballyclare
Bandon
Beaverstown
Beech Park
Black Bush
Blackwood
Bright Castle
Castle Barna
Castle Comer
Castle
Castlebar
Cill Dara
Citywest
Coldwinters
Corrstown
County Cavan
County Longford
Craddockstown
Cruit Island
Deer Park

Donaghadee
Downpatrick
Dungarvan
Dunmurry
Edenmore
Enniscorthy
Fermoy
Forrest Little
Fortwilliam
Fota Island
Foyle International
Greenore
Gweedore
Harbour Point
Hollywood Lakes
Holywood
Kilkee
Kilkeel
Killeen
Killiney
Kinsale
Knockanally
Lisburn
Lucan
Lurgan

Mahee Island
Malahide
Mallow
Milltown
Mount Wolsley
Mullingar
Newlands
Nuremore
Oughterard
Portarlington
Rockmount
Rosecrea
Royal Belfast

Scrabo
Seapoint
Skerries
Spa
St Helens Bay
Stackstown
Tuam
Warrenpoint
Waterford Castle
Waterford
Westmanstown
Wicklow

★

Balbriggan
Cahir Park
Carrickfergus
Castle Hume
Castlewarden
Clonmel
Clontarf
Delvin Castle
Edmondstown
Ennis
Gort
Kilkea Castle
Killeline
Letterkenny
Limerick
Loughrea

Macroom
Monkstown
Mountrath
Muskerry
North West
Old Conna
Open Golf Centre Home of
    Coldwinters
Portadown
Roscommon
Rush
Slade Valley
Strandhill
Swords
The Heath

Munster

Ballybunion Golf Club (Old) ★★★★★

Sandhill Road, Ballybunion, County Kerry
Nearest main town: Limerick

Ballybunion, literally translated as town of the sapling, is a small resort village on the southern side of the Shannon estuary. It is rightly on the itinerary for those mega-rich Americans who come on short golfing tours to these islands. They take in Turnberry, Gleneagles, St Andrews and then Ballybunion Old. Not surprisingly, the price of playing here has gone through the roof, and anyone wanting to pick up some commemorative merchandise of their visit to Ballybunion will have to dig deep to afford the prices in the pro shop.

Ballybunion's remoteness and the sheer size of its dunes make it a honey-pot for all golfers. The dunes at Turnberry and St Andrews are bumps by comparison. Unlike, say, Royal Birkdale, where the dunes tend to flank the fairways, at Ballybunion these often run perpendicular to the line of play. You are driving over them, into them, up them, and onto them. In the words of Christy O'Connor Snr, 'When the wind blows, anyone who breaks 70 here is playing better than he is able to play.'

It is difficult to score well at Ballybunion, simply because the distractions (shiny beaches, crumbling cliffs etc.) are so engaging. As early as the 1st tee you stand looking straight at a graveyard, hardly the uplifting encouragement you need at the start of the round.

By comparison with many other great links, it is a modest opening after the 1st, but things start to get better at the 7th, a par-4 laid out along the shore with a small plateau green clinging to the dunes above the Atlantic. The 10th, another par-4, doglegs its way left, back to the very edge of the ocean, and the 11th has the twin threat of sandhills on the left and the Atlantic to the right.

Some talk of playing Ballybunion as if their life has been changed completely by the experience. Don't listen to the hype: take the course for what it's really worth, an excellent links but one that is surely bettered elsewhere.

Secretary: Mr J. McKenna   Tel: 068 27146
                                Fax: 068 27387
Professional: Mr B. O'Callaghan   Tel: 068 27842

Playing: Midweek: round £35.00; day £80.00. Weekend: round £35.00; day £80.00. Handicap certificate required.

Facilities: Bar: 10.30am–11pm. Food: Lunch and dinner from 10am–9pm. Bar snacks.

Comments: Day fee is round on each course ... What an experience ... Spectacularly beautiful, terrifically enjoyable ... Super course when the wind blows ... Absolute must for all golfers with stunning views and unique holes ... An absolute masterpiece, Tom Watson is right.

Lahinch Golf Club (Old)

Lahinch, County Clare
Nearest main town: Ennis

The small town of Lahinch overlooks Liscannor Bay and the Cliffs of Moher, and its fabric is inextricably interwoven with the life of the golf club – hence its nickname of the Irish St Andrews. It's traditional but very fair, imposing and rewarding, and so natural you'll even see goats milling around the course. They will tell you the weather – if the goats come off the dunes and are sheltering by the clubhouse, don't bother going out, the heavens are about to open.

The Scots introduced golf to Lahinch in 1893, but it was in 1928 that Dr Alister Mackenzie, who had recently completed work in Cypress Point and was soon after to collaborate with Bobby Jones on Augusta, revised the links. Mackenzie was not allowed to touch two holes, the 5th and the 6th. The former, known as Klondyke, is a long par-4 with a second shot that has to clear a mound very much in the fashion of the 16th hole at Southport and Ainsdale. The 6th, 'Dell', is a blind par-3, an anachronism that is not without charm.

The toughest holes at Lahinch are at the end. After the short par-4 13th where a birdie is up for grabs, it just gets better and better. The par-5 14th plays to a landing area that serves the 15th as well, before running up to a green guarded on both sides by treacherous hills and impenetrable rough. You'll need to land the ball on the front of the green at the short par-3 16th before facing up to two cracking finishing holes, with the 18th hole playing across the 5th fairway.

The course has been subject to modifications, but the many faces of Lahinch are the product of the wind off the Atlantic that whistles through the dunes and the huge rocks and the squalls that rush in on many occasions. Members will say you never really can work out the nature of this links, but the bottom line is that if you keep it straight and are familiar with bump-and-run shots, then you cannot go too far wrong.

Secretary:	Mr A. Reardon	Tel: 065 81003
		Fax: 065 81592
Professional:	Mr R. McCavery	Tel: 065 81408

Playing: Midweek: round £45.00; day £55.00. Weekend: round £45.00; day n/a. Handicap certificate required.

Facilities: Bar: 10.30am–11pm. Food: Breakfast, lunch and dinner from 9am–9pm. Bar snacks.

Comments: True golfer's course ... Classic links made even more enjoyable by the friendly atmosphere ... Great old-fashioned links with very springy turf ... The village and course as a unit are completely committed to golf ... A must for all links lovers ... Devilish course with best bunkering ever seen ... Remarkable course on choice piece of land ... Will never forget it.

Old Head Golf Club ★★★★★

Kinsale, County Cork
Nearest main town: Kinsale

After seeing this course for the first time, an American journalist wrote: 'Golfing angels will congregate here and legends will be born.' Gushing it may be, but it is true you will be hard pushed to find a more dramatic course to play golf than Old Head of Kinsale. Indeed, it is probably one of the most exciting courses opened in modern times, tales of its grandeur passing lips in clubhouses across Britain and Ireland and the world each day.

The course sits on a huge rocky peninsula on the south coast of Ireland, its two loops of nine occupying a bulge of land that by rights should have been cut off from the mainland. Golfers cannot help but be faced with stunning views of 300-foot cliffs, especially as most of the greens are perched right on top of them. Such is the scenery that this promontory was included in the Inventory of Outstanding Landscapes in Ireland.

Old Head was opened for play in June 1997. It has five par-5s, five par-3s and eight par-4s, a very modern balance of holes on what is a site fashioned through the centuries. From the back tees, it weighs in at a hefty 7100 yards and has already been mentioned in the same breath as Pebble Beach. Like that famed American course, you will be walking a cliff-top tightrope and in places, such is the prevailing nature of the wind, you will be sending tee shots out across the Atlantic in order to find the fairway when the ball lands. There are few hazards along the fairways at Old Head, as, basically, the wind is the only hazard you need. Indeed, such is the strength of the wind and the inclement weather that affects this place, the course is closed for the winter.

Old Head is destined to become a classic and for golfers travelling to the area to play Fota Island, Cork and Lee Valley, is likely to become the one you play first or last.

Secretary: Mr J. O'Brien   Tel: 021 778444
                                 Fax: 021 778022

Professional: None.

Playing: Midweek: round £90.00; day £150.00. Weekend: round £90.00; day £150.00. Handicap certificate required.

Facilities: Bar: 10.30am–11pm. Food: Breakfast, lunch and dinner from 9am–9pm. Bar snacks.

Comments: Unbelievable location ... Destined to be a classic ... You feel on the edge of the world ... Most exciting course to play in the world at the moment ... In places you simply hit the ball out to sea ... Gobsmacked ... Course shut half the year and on some days is simply unplayable ... Play it now before everyone finds out.

Tralee Golf Club   ★★★★★

West Barrow, Ardfert, County Kerry
Nearest main town: Tralee

Tralee is home to the festival known the world over as the 'Rose of Tralee'. This is a curious event in these politically correct times, where young women from all over the country and the globe come to show off their beauty and, well, their Irishness. If there was to be a swimsuit section, they could do worse than film it on the beach below the 15th tee at the town's golf course, a stunning expanse of sand where the swirling emerald tide gushes through narrow channels to fill inland lagoons.

Tralee Golf Club (or Barrow to those in the know) would certainly win prizes for its natural beauty. It's a youngster compared to most of the other great links courses of the south-west of Ireland. Designed by Arnold Palmer, the course is as individual as they come, a links laid out against some of the most majestic and rugged coastline on the island. It has just about everything – holes practically dropping off into the ocean, deep valleys, flat, downhill, uphill, sidehill holes, tumultuous dunes, views to make you feel lucky that you are alive and a changeable wind to let you know that this a golf course and you have a battle on your hands.

Some rate it too difficult, but that's just because the occasional visitor does not know it that well. Yes, there are some idiosyncratic holes, but where would we be if every course followed a formula? One thing is for sure, the back nine is a roller-coaster ride tempered with some of the finest views afforded from any golf course anywhere.

There are many memorable holes at Tralee, but most name the 12th as the favourite and the toughest. It's a par-4 with a driving area the size of an airstrip between tall, wild grass on the right and rocks on the left. The second shot is played to an elevated green situated on the crater on the dune. On the left of the green is a huge abyss where balls will disappear forever. Then there's the view from the 17th green, in all directions surf crashing against the shore. The band has packed up and left by the 18th, a rather mundane par-4 by comparison to what's gone before, but you've still got the clubhouse to look forward to, one of the newest and best in the area, with views towards the cliff and the beach.

Secretary:	Mr M. O'Brian	Tel: 066 36379
		Fax: 066 36008
Professional:	None.	

Playing: Midweek: round £35.00; day n/a. Weekend: round £35.00; day n/a. Handicap certificate required.

Facilities: Bar: 10.30am–11pm. Food: Lunch and dinner from 10am–11pm. Bar snacks.

Comments: Visually stunning ... Very exciting ... Best back nine in Ireland ... Memorable holes ... What views, what greens, what a privilege to play there ... Best ever welcome ... Arrived at a busy time and was immediately dispatched to the 1st tee ... Lunch and drinks were sent out by buggy ... Palmer really worked his magic here.

Adare Manor Golf Club   ★★★★

Adare, County Limerick
Nearest main town: Limerick

Secretary:	Mr M. Palne	Tel: 061 396204
Professional:	None.	

Playing: Midweek: round £15.00; day n/a. Weekend: round £20.00; day n/a. Handicap certificate required.

Facilities: Bar: 10.30am–11pm. Food: Bar snacks.

Comments: A Robert Trent Jones classic ... Huge moulding gives this a very un-Irish feel ... Not your typical Irish course ... Very American, but who cares? ... Very hard going, like the K-Club ... Give the course two more years and it will be out of this world ... Superb new course with good bunkers and plenty of water ... Greens soft spikes only.

Ballybunion Golf Club (Cashen)   ★★★★★

Sandhill Road, Ballybunion, County Kerry
Nearest main town: Limerick

Secretary:	Mr J. McKenna	Tel: 068 27146
		Fax: 068 27387
Professional:	Mr B. O'Callaghan	Tel: 068 27842

Playing: Midweek: round £60.00; day £80.00. Weekend: round £60.00; day £80.00. Handicap certificate required.

Facilities: Bar: 10.30am–11pm. Food: Lunch and dinner from 10am–9pm. Bar snacks.

Comments: Day fee is round on each course ... Great job by Robert Trent Jones ... Even though it was designed by an American, there is a magically Irish feel to this course ... Old Course knocks it into a cocked hat ... More difficult than the Old ... A lot bleaker than the Old Course but just as enjoyable ... Amazing that this new course should feel so ancient.

Ballyheigue Castle Golf Club   ★★★

Ballyheigue, Tralee, County Kerry
Nearest main town: Tralee

Secretary:	Mr J. Broderick	Tel: 066 33555
		Fax: 066 33147
Professional:	None.	

Playing: Midweek: round £17.00; day n/a. Weekend: round n/a; day n/a. Handicap certificate required.

Facilities: Bar: None. Food:

Comments: Nine championship-standard golf holes are laid out on approximately 100 acres of beautiful rolling parkland, overlooking the magnificent Ballyheigue beach and the Brandon Mountains in the distant background.

Ballykisteen Golf & Country Club

Monard, County Tipperary
Nearest main town: Tipperary

Secretary:	Mrs J. Ryan	Tel: 062 33333
		Fax: 062 33711
Professional:	Mr D. Reddan	

Playing: Midweek: round £20.00; day n/a. Weekend: round £25.00; day n/a. Handicap certificate required.

Facilities: Bar: 10.30am–11pm. Food: Lunch and dinner from 11am–9pm. Bar snacks.

Comments: Warm, Irish welcome, people, food and course top class ... Water in play on ten holes ... Great par-3 15th ... Seemingly unnatural course that rewards all types of shot ... In ten years' time everyone will be talking about this course ... Young greens but fast.

Bandon Golf Club

Castlebernard, Bandon, County Cork
Nearest main town: Bandon

Secretary:	Mr P. Kehoe	Tel: 023 41111
		Fax: 023 44690
Professional:	Mr P. O'Boyle	Tel: 023 42224

Playing: Midweek: round on application; day on application. Weekend: round n/a; day n/a. Handicap certificate required.

Facilities: Bar: None. Food:

Comments: Set in the ground of Castlebernard Castle, this well established parkland course is renowned for its scenic setting in the beautiful valley of Bandon ... Accurate driving is essential here.

Bantry Bay Golf Club ★★★

Donemark, Bantry, County Cork
Nearest main town: Bantry (Cork City 60 miles)

Secretary:	Miss L. O'Shea	Tel: 027 50579
		Fax: 027 50579
Professional:	None.	

Playing: Midweek: round £20.00; day £30.00. Weekend: round £20.00; day £30.00. Handicap certificate required.

Facilities: Bar: 10am–closing time (summer months). Food: Restaurant open May–October.

Comments: Idyllically set at the head of Bantry Bay, this is one of the most spectacular and scenic courses in Ireland … Extended to 18 holes in 1997 under the guidance of Christy O'Connor Jr. O'Connor Jr remarks, 'The architect of this course was not me but Mother Nature – I just gave her a helping hand!'

Beaufort Golf Club   ★★★★

Churchtown, Beaufort, County Kerry
Nearest main town: Killarney

Secretary: Mr C. Kelly   Tel: 064 44440
                                       Fax: 064 44752

Professional: Mr H. Duggan

Playing: Midweek: round £25.00; day £35.00. Weekend: round £33.00; day £46.00. Handicap certificate required.

Facilities: Bar: 10.30am–11pm. Food: Lunch and dinner from 10am–9pm. Bar snacks.

Comments: Superb setting with the McGillicuddy Reeks forming an impressive backdrop … Historic course with ruins, natural hazards, deep bunkers, impressive foliage and multi-tiered greens … Blind shots make this so difficult.

Cahir Park Golf Club   ★

Kilcommon, Cahir, County Tipperary
Nearest main town: Cahir

Secretary: Mr J. Costigan   Tel: 052 41146 (H)
Professional: Mr M. Joseph   Tel: 052 41474
                                       Fax: 052 41474

Playing: Midweek: round n/a; day £15.00. Weekend: round n/a; day £15.00. Handicap certificate required.

Facilities: Bar: 10am–11pm. Food: Catering facilities available, must pre-book by phone.

Comments: Set in prime parkland, these nine holes are carved out of part of the old Cahir Park Estate ... The feature hole is the par-4 7th which is bordered on the right hand side by the River Suir.

Castlebar Golf Club

Hawthorn Avenue, Rocklands, Castlebar, County Mayo
Nearest main town: Castlebar

Secretary: Mr E. Lonergan   Tel: 094 21649
Professional: None.

Playing: Midweek: round £20.00; day n/a. Weekend: round £25.00; day n/a. Handicap certificate required.

Facilities: Bar: 9am–11.30pm. Food: noon–8pm.

Comments: Not all that long, but very enjoyable to play ... Well established parkland layout that's not too difficult ... Very friendly welcome ... Excellent value.

Castletroy Golf Club

Castletroy, Limerick, County Limerick
Nearest main town: Limerick

Secretary: Mr L. Hayes   Tel: 061 335261
                                    Fax: 061 335373
Professional: None.

Playing: Midweek: round £22.00; day n/a. Weekend: round £25.00; day n/a. Handicap certificate required.

Facilities: Bar: 10.30am–11pm. Food: Lunch and dinner from 10am–9pm.

Comments: Very short course that can be very flattering on your score ... Don't play it to improve your game, just for fun ... Cheap and cheerful.

Charleville Golf Club ★★★

Smiths Road, Charleville, County Cork
Nearest main town: Charleville

Secretary: Mr M. Keane   Tel: 063 81257
                                         Fax: 063 81274

Professional: None.

Playing: Midweek: round £15.00; day £18.00. Weekend: round
                    £20.00; day £25.00. Handicap certificate required.

Facilities: Bar: 11am–11pm. Food: Lunch and dinner from
                    11am–9pm. Bar snacks.

Comments: Busy parkland ... Short but really nice ... Not particu-
                    larly well regarded in Cork.

Clonmel Golf Club   ★

Lyreanearla, Mountain Road, Clonmel, County Tipperary
Nearest main town: Clonmel

Secretary: Mrs A. Myles-Keating Tel: 052 24050
                                         Fax: 052 24050

Professional: Mr R. Hayes   Tel: 052 24050

Playing: Midweek: round £18.00; day n/a. Weekend: round
                    £20.00; day n/a. Handicap certificate required.

Facilities: Bar: 10.30am–11pm. Food: Bar snacks.

Comments: Open, bland course ... Very short on length and interest
                    ... Gives you the freedom to open your shoulders off the
                    tee ... A real driver's course with room for error ...
                    Inland course of little standing.

Cork Golf Club

Little Island, Cork, County Cork
Nearest main town: Cork

Secretary: Mr M. Sands   Tel: 021 353451
                                         Fax: 021 353410

Professional: Mr P. Hickey   Tel: 021 353421

Playing: Midweek: round £40.00; day £40.00. Weekend: round
                    £45.00; day n/a. Handicap certificate required.

Facilities: Bar: 10.30am–11pm. Food: Breakfast, lunch and
                    dinner from 9am–9pm. Bar snacks.

Comments: Excellent condition and plenty of birdie chances ... Touched by the hand of Alistair Mackenzie ... Great club with course to match ... Not very exhilarating, but a fair technical challenge ... Prime condition ... Play here on the way to the Old Head of Kinsale further south.

County Tipperary Golf & Country Club ★★★★

Dundrum House Hotel, Dundrum, Cashel, County Tipperary
Nearest main town: Cashel

Secretary: Mr W. Crowe   Tel: 062 71116
Fax: 062 71366

Professional: None.

Playing: Midweek: round £20.00; day n/a. Weekend: round £24.00; day n/a. Handicap certificate required.

Facilities: Bar: 10.30am–11pm. Food: Breakfast, lunch and dinner from 7am–10pm. Bar snacks.

Comments: Back nine is where course really impresses ... Good use of water on some holes ... Unique Irish course designed by Philip Walton ... You can feel the American influences here ... Nice use of man-made hazards ... Hotel, converted from 18th-century manor, marks this a quality weekend getaway destination.

Dingle Golf Club ★★★★

Ballyoughheragh, Tralee, County Kerry
Nearest main town: Tralee

Secretary: Mr T. O'Shea   Tel: 066 56408
Fax: 066 56409

Professional: Mr D. O'Connor   Tel: 066 56225

Playing: Midweek: round n/a; day £25.00. Weekend: round n/a; day £35.00.

Facilities: Bar: 11am–11pm. Food: Lunch and dinner from 10am–6pm. Bar snacks.

Comments: Magical setting overlooking Dingle Bay ... New links that's so exciting ... Wind wreaks havoc here ... Keep the ball as low as you can ... Links that simply teases you at every turn ... Evocative ... Preferred it to more prestigious courses in the area ... Very welcoming ... Very sandy and difficult ... Love this place ... A natural course with fine character.

Dooks Golf Club ★★★★

Glenbeigh, County Kerry
Nearest main town: Kerry

Secretary:	Mr M. Shanahan	Tel: 066 9768205
		Fax: 066 9768476

Professional: None.

Playing: Midweek: round £25.00; day £35.00. Weekend: round £25.00; day £35.00. Handicap certificate required.

Facilities: Bar: 10.30am–11pm. Food: Lunch and dinner from noon–9pm. Bar snacks.

Comments: Not to be missed ... Tough links with friendly welcome and good food ... Always easy to get a game, lovely scenery and friendly members ... Gem of a course with interesting holes and warm welcome.

Dromoland Castle Golf Club ★★★

Newmarket-on-Fergus, County Clare
Nearest main town: Limerick

Secretary:	Mr J. O'Halloran	Tel: 061 368444
		Fax: 061 368498
Professional:	Mr P. Murphy	Tel: 061 368951

Playing: Midweek: round £28.00; day n/a. Weekend: round £33.00; day n/a. Handicap certificate required.

Facilities: Bar: 10.30pm–11pm. Food: Lunch and dinner from 10.30am–9pm. Bar snacks.

Comments: Set in the grounds of a magnificent castle ... Subtle greens with hard-to-read breaks ... Lack of length countered by blind tee shots and sculpted greens ... Not given the recognition it deserves ... Played badly but eyes were open to the quality of the course ... Rolling fairways ... Greens a pleasure to putt on.

Dungarvan Golf Club ★★

Knocknagranagh, Dungarvan, County Waterford
Nearest main town: Waterford

Secretary:	Mr T. Whelan	Tel: 058 44707
		Fax: 058 44113
Professional:	Mr D. Hayes	Tel: 058 44707

Playing: Midweek: round £17.00; day £25.00. Weekend: round £22.00; day £30.00. Handicap certificate required.

Facilities: Bar: 10.30am–11pm. Food: Lunch and dinner from noon–9pm. Bar snacks.

Comments: Excellent variety of holes on a course that is improving all the time ... Comeragh Mountains provide the backdrop ... Weak course where all the hazards are man-made ... Average standard on not too difficult course.

Ennis Golf Club ★

Drumbiggle Road, Bodyke, County Clare
Nearest main town: Ennis

Secretary:	Mr J. Normoyle	Tel: 065 24074
		Fax: 065 41848
Professional:	Mr M. Ward	Tel: 065 20690

Playing: Midweek: round £18.00; day n/a. Weekend: round £18.00; day n/a. Handicap certificate required.

Facilities: Bar: 10.30am–11pm. Food: Bar snacks.

Comments: Basic course with few features ... Course can get heavy underfoot ... Enniscrone yes, Ennis no ... Very picturesque ... Part mature woodland, part downland ... Cheerful, straightforward layout ... Good for friendly and family golf.

Faithlegg House Golf Club ★★★

Faithlegg House, Faithlegg, County Waterford
Nearest main town: Waterford

Secretary:	Mr V. McGreevy	Tel: 051 382241
Professional:	Mr T. Higgins	Tel: 051 382688

Playing: Midweek: round n/a; day n/a. Weekend: round n/a; day n/a. Handicap certificate required. Green fees on application.

Facilities: Bar: 11am–11pm. Food: Lunch from noon–5pm. Dinner by arrangement.

Comments: Mature trees give this course an established feel ... Not always in top condition but I always return ... A little tricked up with hazards not visible from the tee ... Be on your guard, this course will catch you.

Fermoy Golf Club   ★★

Corrin, Fermoy, County Cork
Nearest main town: Fermoy

Secretary: Ms K. Murphy   Tel: 025 32694
                                        Fax: 025 33072
Professional: Mr B. Moriarty   Tel: 025 31472

Playing: Midweek: round £13.00; day n/a. Weekend: round £16.00; day n/a. Handicap certificate required.

Facilities: Bar: 11am–11.30pm in the summer. Food: Food is available on request.

Comments: Fermoy Golf Club has provided over a century of first class golf to its members ... The heavily wooded heathland course offers a great variety of holes, notably the dogleg 14th across a ravine ... Renowned for the excellence of its greens and spectacular views of the Avondhu countryside.

Fota Island Golf Club   ★★

Carrigtwohill, Cork City, County Cork
Nearest main town: Cork City 9 miles

Secretary: Mr K. Mulcahy   Tel: 021 883700
                   (Manager)   Fax: 021 883713
Professional: Mr K. Morris   Tel: 021 883710

Playing: Midweek: round Mon–Thu – summer £45.00, winter £30.00; day n/a. Weekend: round Fri-Sun – summer £55.00, winter £40.00; day n/a. Handicap certificate required.

Facilities: Bar: 10am–11pm. Food: Bar food available and also a restaurant.

Comments: Superb setting in the middle of Cork Harbour ... Very traditional style layout ... Classic setting with pot bunkers a-plenty ... Some of the double greens can leave you with huge first putts ... Loved the layout ... Very challenging and plays long and difficult when the wind gets up ... Lovely clubhouse with nice restaurant and friendly staff.

Harbour Point Golf Club ★★

Clash, Little Island, County Cork
Nearest main town: Cork

Secretary: Ms N. O'Connell   Tel: 021 353094
                                  Fax: 021 354408

Professional: None.

Playing: Midweek: round £15.00; day £20.00. Weekend: round n/a; day n/a. Handicap certificate required.

Facilities: Bar: None. Food:

Comments: Set by the banks of the River Lee at Cork's scenic harbour this exciting design demands a full range of shots from the golfer ... Excellent driving range and wonderful hospitality in the atmospheric clubhouse.

Kenmare Golf Club ★★★

Kenmare, County Waterford
Nearest main town: Killarney

Secretary: Mr M. MacGearailt   Tel: 064 41291
                                     Fax: 064 42061

Professional: None.

Playing: Midweek: round £16.00; day £26.00. Weekend: round £16.00; day £26.00. Handicap certificate required.

Facilities: Bar: 10.30am–11pm. Food: Bar snacks.

Comments: Not a difficult course but overall craic makes it a pleasant walk ... Expanded to 18 holes five years ago ... Par-3 17th a fun hole ... Nine holes in the valley very charming ... Small course with a lot going for it ... Open course, very enjoyable for the higher handicapper.

Kilkee Golf Club ★★

East End, Kilkee, County Clare
Nearest main town: Ennis

Secretary: Mr P. McInerney   Tel: 065 9056977
Professional: None.

Playing: Midweek: round £20.00; day n/a. Weekend: round
                    £20.00; day n/a. Handicap certificate required.

Facilities: Bar: All day. Food: Available on request.

Comments: Some truly dramatic holes which overlook the Atlantic
                    Ocean ... You can walk to the course in under 15
                    minutes from the centre of Kilkee ... Well established,
                    classic links course layout running along the top of
                    the cliffs ... Excellent facilities and outstanding value golf.

Killarney Golf Club (Killeen) ★★★★

Mahoney's Point, Killarney, County Kerry
Nearest main town: Killarney

Secretary: Mr T. Prendergast   Tel: 064 31034
                                            Fax: 064 33065
Professional: Mr T. Coveney   Tel: 064 31615

Playing: Midweek: round £20.00; day n/a. Weekend: round
                    £38.00; day n/a. Handicap certificate required.

Facilities: Bar: 10.30am–11pm. Food: Lunch and dinner from
                    10am–9pm. Bar snacks.

Comments: Lovely surroundings to a very special course ... From the
                    back tees fairways look very narrow ... An amazing chal-
                    lenge with trouble everywhere ... Wonderful, scenic
                    course, not overlong for amateurs ... Great setting with
                    course in superb condition ... Epitome of the idyllic –
                    great courses, great people and great food and drink.

Killarney Golf Club (Mahoney's Point) ★★★★

Mahoney's Point, Killarney, County Kerry
Nearest main town: Killarney

Secretary: Mr T. Prendergast   Tel: 064 31034
                                            Fax: 064 33065
Professional: Mr T. Coveney   Tel: 064 31615

Playing: Midweek: round £38.00; day n/a. Weekend: round £38.00; day n/a. Handicap certificate required.

Facilities: Bar: 10.30am–11pm. Food: Lunch and dinner from 10am–9pm. Bar snacks.

Comments: Course in exceptional condition with great views everywhere ... Finishes with the toughest of tough par-3s ... Great finish ... Doesn't compare to the Killeen ... Play them both in the same day – an awesome, life-changing experience.

Killeline Golf Club ★

Newcastle West, County Limerick
Nearest main town: Limerick

Secretary: Mr J. McCoy   Tel: 069 61600
                              Fax: 069 62853

Professional: To be appointed.

Playing: Midweek: round £12.00; day n/a. Weekend: round £12.00; day n/a. Handicap certificate required.

Facilities: Bar: 10.30am–11pm. Food: Breakfast, lunch and dinner from 9am–9pm. Bar snacks.

Comments: Basic layout set in the Golden Vale ... Simple course but there is a premium on accuracy ... Reasonable value for parkland course.

Killorglin Golf Club

Steelroe, Killorglin, County Kerry
Nearest main town: Killarney

Secretary: Mr B. Dodd   Tel: 066 61979
                             Fax: 066 61437

Professional: None.

Playing: Midweek: round £14.00; day n/a. Weekend: round £16.00; day n/a. Handicap certificate required.

Facilities: Bar: 10.30am–11pm. Food: Bar snacks.

Comments: Played it when first opened – great ... Fairly easy despite small greens ... Overlooking Dingle Bay, this is cheap and cheerful ... Homely place where staff will arrange anything for you ... Great welcome at this testing, enjoyable course.

Kinsale Golf Club   ★★

Farrangalway, Kinsale, County Cork
Nearest main town: Kinsale 4 miles, Cork 18 miles

Secretary:	Mr P. Murray	Tel: 021 774722
	(Manager)	Fax: 021 773114
Professional:	Mr G. Broderick	Tel: 021 773258
		Fax: 021 779714

Playing: Midweek: round £22.00; day n/a. Weekend: round £27.00; day n/a. Handicap certificate required.

Facilities: Bar: 11am–11.30pm. Food: 9am–9pm.

Comments: Naturally rolling terrain and excellent draining soil are the ideal ingredients for a good course ... Pleasant setting ... New course which opened in 1995 is now maturing nicely ... Enjoyable parkland golf ... Old 9-hole layout is fun to play.

Lahinch Golf Club (Castle)   ★★★★

Lahinch, County Clare
Nearest main town: Ennis

Secretary:	Mr A. Reardon	Tel: 065 81003
		Fax: 065 81592
Professional:	Mr R. McCavery	Tel: 065 81408

Playing: Midweek: round £25.00; day £25.00. Weekend: round £25.00; day n/a. Handicap certificate required.

Facilities: Bar: 10.30am–11pm. Food: Breakfast, lunch and dinner from 9am–9pm. Bar snacks.

Comments: Classic links track which is worth a visit in its own right ... Loved it ... Perfect partner to the Old Course ... Under-rated with holes that would not be out of place on the Old ... Shorter and easier, but a nice test.

Lee Valley Golf & Country Club   ★★★

Clashanure, Ovens, Kinsale, County Cork
Nearest main town: Cork

Secretary:	Mr J. Reilly	Tel: 021 331721
	(Manager)	Fax: 021 331695
Professional:	Mr J. Savage	Tel: 021 331758

Playing: Midweek: round £27.00; day n/a. Weekend: round £29.00; day n/a. Handicap certificate required.

Facilities: Bar: 10.30am–11pm. Food: Breakfast, lunch and dinner from 9am–9pm. Bar snacks.

Comments: New course designed by Christy O'Connor Jr ... Very busy ... A course that caters for every standard of player ... Take your time over every shot – you will have to ... Crowded course, not what I wanted from golf in Ireland ... Hilly, parkland course ... Facilities second to none ... State-of-the-art facilities better than the course.

Limerick Golf Club   ★

Limerick, County Limerick
Nearest main town: Limerick

Secretary: Mr D. McDonogh   Tel: 061 415146
                                          Fax: 061 415146
Professional: To be appointed   Tel: 061 412492

Playing: Midweek: round £22.50; day n/a. Weekend: round n/a; day n/a. Handicap certificate required.

Facilities: Bar: 10.30am–11pm. Food: Lunch and dinner from 10am–9pm.

Comments: Parkland course with friendly, large membership ... Fair value for traditional parkland layout ... If you're in the area play Limerick County, not this one.

Limerick County Golf & Country Club

Ballyneety, County Limerick
Nearest main town: Limerick

Secretary: Mr A. Fallow   Tel: 061 351881
                                          Fax: 061 351384
Professional: Mr P. Murphy   Tel: 061 351874

Playing: Midweek: round £20.00; day £30.00. Weekend: round £25.00; day £35.00. Handicap certificate required.

Facilities: Bar: 10.30am–11pm. Food: Lunch and dinner from 10am–9pm.

Comments: The bar is out of this world ... A Des Smyth design, fairly unusual for a modern course ... Blind drives and deep bunkers give an old-style feel to a new course ... Unusual clubhouse ... Great venue for matchplay golf.

Macroom Golf Club

Lacaduu, Macroom, County Cork
Nearest main town: Cork/Killarney

Secretary: Mrs D. Cronin   Tel: 026 41072
                                           Fax: 026 41391

Professional: None.

Playing: Midweek: round £15.00; day n/a. Weekend: round £18.00; day n/a. Handicap certificate required.

Facilities: Bar: 10.30am–11pm. Food: Food is available all day.

Comments: Pleasant parkland layout ... Located quite close to the town centre ... Not overly testing, but enjoyable to play ... Good value for money ... Friendly welcome.

Mallow Golf Club

Ballyellis, Mallow, County Cork
Nearest main town: Mallow

Secretary: Mrs I. Howell   Tel: 022 21145
                                           Fax: 022 42501

Professional: Mr S. Conway

Playing: Midweek: round £20.00; day n/a. Weekend: round £25.00; day n/a. Handicap certificate required.

Facilities: Bar: 10.30am–11pm. Food: Breakfast, lunch and dinner from 11am–9pm. Bar snacks.

Comments: Tree-lined parkland beauty ... Nice condition for this friendly club ... Nothing spectacular, but good honest golf.

Monkstown Golf Club   ★

Parkgarriffe, Monkstown, County Cork
Nearest main town: Cork

Secretary:	Mr J. Long	Tel: 021 841376
		Fax: 021 841376
Professional:	Mr B. Murphy	Tel: 021 841686

Playing: Midweek: round £23.00; day £23.00. Weekend: round £26.00; day n/a. Handicap certificate required.

Facilities: Bar: 10.30am–11pm. Food: Lunch and dinner from noon–9pm.

Comments: Scenic views of Cork Harbour ... Bunkers absolutely everywhere ... Bizarre bunkering ... Parkland course where accuracy is your watchword ... Fair value on this testing track.

Muskerry Golf Club   ★

Carrigrohane, County Cork
Nearest main town: Blarney

Secretary:	Mr J. Moynihan	Tel: 021 385297
		Fax: 021 385297
Professional:	Mr W. Lehane	Tel: 021 381445

Playing: Midweek: round £23.00; day n/a. Weekend: round n/a; day n/a. Handicap certificate required.

Facilities: Bar: 10.30am–11pm. Food: Bar snacks.

Comments: Epitome of golf in Ireland ... Good value course, good craic ... Great welcome ... Course is so-so but the bar is always buzzing ... 16th and 17th across the river are the best holes.

Parknasilla Golf Club

Parknasilla, Sneem, County Kerry
Nearest main town: Sneem

Secretary:	Mr M. Walsh	Tel: 064 45122
		Fax: 064 45323
Professional:	Mr C. McCarthy	

Playing: Midweek: round n/a; day £15.00. Weekend: round n/a; day £15.00. Handicap certificate required.

Facilities: Bar: 10.30am–11pm. Food: Breakfast, lunch and dinner from 9am–9pm. Bar snacks.

Comments: Best 9-hole course ever played ... Location, location, location ... Unique 9-hole course of beauty and tranquillity ... Overlooking Kenmare Bay.

Rosecrea Golf Club   ★★

Derryvale, Rosecrea, County Tipperary
Nearest main town: Rosecrea

Secretary: Mr S. Crofton   Tel: 050 521130
Professional: None.

Playing: Midweek: round £14.00; day n/a. Weekend: round £17.00; day n/a. Handicap certificate required.

Facilities: Bar: 10am–11.30pm. Food: Food is available on request.

Comments: Situated on the main Dublin/Limerick road, Rosecrea is an ideal place to break the journey to play a game and enjoy a snack lunch ... A special feature of the course is the variety of the short holes, but the signature hole is without doubt the tree-lined par-5 7th, known locally as 'The Burma Road'.

Shannon Golf Club   ★★★

Shannon, County Clare
Nearest main town: Shannon

Secretary: Mr M. Corry   Tel: 061 471849
                                        Fax: 061 471507
Professional: Mr A. Pyke   Tel: 061 471551

Playing: Midweek: round £22.00; day £22.00. Weekend: round £27.00; day £27.00. Handicap certificate required.

Facilities: Bar: 10.30am–11pm. Food: Breakfast, lunch and dinner from 9am–9pm. Bar snacks.

Comments: A mix of links and parkland ... Highlight is the 216-yard par-3 over the estuary ... Very tight course with character ... Water hazards the primary defence ... Rough can get high ... Pop off the plane and onto the course ... Tight, but you are lost without the driver ... Site of Greg Norman's famous 370-yard drive. ... Front nine a hellish challenge.

Thurles Golf Course

Turtulla, Thurles, County Tipperary
Nearest main town: Thurles

Secretary:	Mr L. Purcell	Tel: 050 421983
		Fax: 050 424647
Professional:	Mr S. Hunt	

Playing: Midweek: round £18.00; day n/a. Weekend: round n/a; day n/a. Handicap certificate required.

Facilities: Bar: None. Food: None.

Comments: A well-respected test of golf, Thurles has played host to national and provincial championships at many levels ... Each hole has its own individual character, but the four demanding par-3 holes are particularly noteworthy.

Tramore Golf Club

Newtown Hill, Tramore, County Waterford
Nearest main town: Waterford

Secretary:	Mr J. Cox	Tel: 051 386170
		Fax: 051 390961
Professional:	Mr D. Kiely	Tel: 051 871395

Playing: Midweek: round £25.00; day £37.00. Weekend: round £30.00; day n/a. Handicap certificate required.

Facilities: Bar: 10.30am–11pm. Food: Breakfast, lunch and dinner from 9am–9pm. Bar snacks.

Comments: Great experience both on and off the course ... Stormy weather has been known ... Very exposed and cold ... Welcoming club with well-groomed course ... Fair test for club golfer ... Lovely set-up at this club with warm, friendly members.

Waterford Golf Club ★★

Newrath, Waterford, County Waterford
Nearest main town: Waterford

Secretary:	Mr J. Condon	Tel: 051 876748
		Fax: 051 853405
Professional:	None.	Tel: 051 856568

Playing: Midweek: round £22.00; day n/a. Weekend: round £25.00; day n/a. Handicap certificate required.

Facilities: Bar: 10.30am–11pm. Food: Lunch and dinner from noon–9pm. Bar snacks.

Comments: Fairly dour parkland course ... Had to wait until the 18th for the best hole ... Overshadowed by the other Waterford (Castle) ... Pleasant enough, but I like a challenge ... Humdrum parkland course ... Fine day out and the company is excellent.

Waterford Castle Golf Club   ★★

The Island, Waterford, County Waterford
Nearest main town: Waterford

Secretary: Mr D. Brennan   Tel: 051 871633
                                          Fax: 051 871634

Professional: None.

Playing: Midweek: round £25.00; day n/a. Weekend: round £29.00; day n/a. Handicap certificate required.

Facilities: Bar: 10.30am–11pm. Food: Bar snacks.

Comments: Des Smyth design ... On-site hotel a real treat, albeit expensive ... Large greens ... Unremarkable land on which to build a course ... Course sits on island in the River Suir ... A flat, featureless course ... Wide open – get your driver out ... Clever design ... With such flat, boring land it's a credit to Smyth for his design.

Waterville Golf Club   ★★★★

Ring of Kerry, Waterville, County Kerry
Nearest main town: Waterville

Secretary: Mr N. Cronin   Tel: 066 74102
                                          Fax: 066 74482

Professional: Mr L. Higgins

Playing: Midweek: round £60.00; day n/a. Weekend: round £60.00; day n/a. Handicap certificate required.

Facilities: Bar: 10.30am–11pm. Food: Lunch and dinner from 10am–9pm. Bar snacks.

Comments: One of the greatest courses in the world ... The best links in the world ... Pro shop rips off the tourist but otherwise an exceptionally good course ... Remote but worth the trip for some holes of great beauty and thought ... Back nine are as good as it gets ... Overpriced, over-rated, overplayed and overpopulated with slow players.

West Waterford Golf Club   ★★★

Dungarvan, County Waterford
Nearest main town: Waterford

Secretary: Mr A. Spratt   Tel: 058 43216
                                           Fax: 058 44343
Professional: None.

Playing: Midweek: round £20.00; day n/a. Weekend: round £25.00; day n/a. Handicap certificate required. Green fees on application.

Facilities: Bar: 10.30am–11pm. Food: Lunch and dinner from 10am–9pm. Bar snacks.

Comments: Excellent greens for what is a young course ... Most natural course ... Contrasting nines ... Set by the Brickey River ... Panoramic views of County Waterford ... Great Irish welcome.

Leinster

Mount Juliet Golf Club ★★★★★

Kilkenny, Thomastown, County Kilkenny
Nearest main town: Kilkenny

Mount Juliet is blessed with some of the finest natural scenery Ireland has to offer: the outcroppings of the Kilkenny countryside, ancient trees, gullies, copses of trees and the furious rushing of the River Nore which is rich in salmon and trout. It is one of the best parkland courses in the country and was designed by none other than Jack Nicklaus.

That's not to say that it has been without criticism. Many say you could transplant this course to any country in the world and it would not look out of place. They claim the excessive moulding, shifting and manipulation of the landscape is completely out of place with the feel and look of this corner of Ireland. In short, Mount Juliet is an artificial course with no soul.

Whether you take this view or not, you cannot fault its condition. One journalist noted that the fairways are made from the same material as the carpets laid down when Prince Charles attends movie premieres, and that, even in the dead of winter, is hard to argue with. There are regiments of maintenance workers grooming the course and you can see golfers almost embarrassed to take a divot out of the fairways.

It is also very fair, some might say easy. Off the tee there is little trouble with wide, generous fairways, and even the greens are large. Even the majestic oak and lime trees that pepper the landscape rarely affect the line of shots into the greens. Nicklaus designs have become more lenient, but it seems there has been a policy that Mount Juliet should be fun, and you should not walk off the course hanging your head like a tired dog.

Water is the main form of defence at Mount Juliet, fronting the par-3 3rd and the par-4 13th. It also protects the 18th, a climatic finish that sums up everything about this modern course.

Secretary:	Mrs K. McCann (Golf Director)	Tel: 056 24455 Fax: 056 73019
Professional:	Mr M. Reid	Tel: 056 730063
Playing:	Midweek: round £70.00; day n/a. Weekend: round £75.00; day n/a. Handicap certificate required.	

Facilities: Bar: 10.30am–11pm. Food: Breakfast, lunch and dinner from 9am–9pm. Bar snacks.

Comments: What every golf course should aspire to ... Best parkland course in Europe ... One of the best new courses in Ireland ... A Nicklaus cracker ... Doesn't necessarily fit into the landscape but good nonetheless ... Vast contoured greens ... One of Jack's best ... Didn't want to go home ... Basic Nicklaus fare, very unnatural ... Cracking par-3 3rd.

Portmarnock Golf Club (Old) ★★★★★

Portmarnock, County Dublin
Nearest main town: Dublin

Few courses are blessed with the natural magnificence of Portmarnock. Set on a long tongue of links land between the Irish Sea and an inland tidal bay, Portmarnock is magnificently cut off from the world, a private playground for golfers in search of hidden delights. The holes run through dune grasses and are completely at the mercy of the wind, which rushes in from the sea quickly changing the moods and toughness of the challenge.

Portmarnock is relatively flat and devoid of any blind shots, but that does not mean the course is monotonous or boring. Instead, you will find a collection of holes that are very exciting, ranging from short holes that require great thought and clever execution of shots, to long holes where brute strength and a daredevil game plan will pay dividends.

Never is this more clearly evident than at the 6th, one of the best holes on the front nine but long at 586 yards. Along its dimpled fairways and valleys, it can be three woods to reach the green, so big hitters are at an advantage. But immediately at the 7th, the emphasis changes with a short hole played into a dell, where you really need to get a feel for the shot.

This delicate balance continues around the turn with more good examples at the 14th, a shortish par-4 with a second shot to a long plateau green among the dunes, and the 15th, a brutish par-3 where, depending on the wind, you will have to set the ball off over the out-of-bounds line and bring it back in on the wind. From there, it is a cracking finish, with the 17th a penal par-4 where you'll do well to stay out of the bunkers and the 18th a fine hole, although it has lost some of its eccentricity since the home green was moved from hard by the clubhouse.

On a fine day there are few better places in Ireland to play golf than at Portmarnock. And with the new Portmarnock Links nearby, you don't need much more encouragement.

Secretary:	Mr J. Quigley	Tel: 01 846 2968
		Fax: 01 846 2601
Professional:	Mr J. Purcell	Tel: 01 846 2634

Playing: Midweek: round £70.00; day n/a. Weekend: round £90.00; day n/a. Handicap certificate required.

Facilities: Bar: 10.30am–11pm. Food: Lunch and dinner from 11am–9pm. Bar snacks.

Comments: Brilliant course and an outstanding pro shop ... Classic links that does not suffer fools gladly ... Not a patch on County Down or Sligo ... Had the time of my life ... Who could criticise this outstanding piece of natural golfing terrain? ... Expected a lot but nothing prepared me for this ... Quite simply the best course in the British Isles.

Portmarnock Hotel and Golf Links   ★★★★★

Portmarnock, Dublin, County Dublin
Nearest main town: Portmarnock

If you hit a slice at the opening hole at Portmarnock Links then you might be dead before you've really started, since your ball is likely to land in the ancient and overgrown graveyard of a twelfth-century Cistercian church ruin. Here, the dark grey memorial stones peer over the old wall and scowl at passing fourballs. To glance at them is to look back into history, and history can be found here in every nook and cranny.

Portmarnock Links was designed by Bernhard Langer and is a new course, although the land on which it lies saw the first golf played on this particular peninsula. The Jameson family, of whiskey fame, had a few holes here even before the great old course at Portmarnock was inaugurated over a century ago. It is tough and uncompromising into the prevailing wind and tricky when the wind is at your back – everything a links course should be. Langer has done an admirable job, although it should be said that the course doesn't really produce its best form until the 8th hole. It is the back nine that hugs the coastline and makes full use of the craggy sand dunes that march away from the hotel and make you wish to play there again.

The 8th is a short, acute dogleg, which is full of character and reachable with a long iron. The green lies beyond a severe dip and is protected on the left by a small, well-like bunker akin to the 'Devil's Asshole' on the 10th at Pine Valley. The 12th is another good hole, playing to a partially hidden green that is devilishly difficult to hit, while the 15th is a dogleg right to a green nestled in an amphitheatre of dunes.

Clues to the historical links lie around every corner of this course, with marks scored on the tee markers to commemorate the local druids, and even the rooms in the luxurious hotel name-check important figures in Portmarnock's history including aviation pioneer Amy Johnson and St Marnock.

Secretary: Mrs M. Cassidy (Golf Director)
Tel: 01 846 1800
Fax: 01 846 1077

Professional: None.

Playing: Midweek: round £55.00; day n/a. Weekend: round £55.00; day n/a. Handicap certificate required.

Facilities: Bar: 11am–11pm. Food: Breakfast, lunch and dinner from 9am–11pm. Bar snacks.

Comments: New links, a real credit to designers ... This course completely devoured me ... Better than the Old course ... Golf this good is rare ... Have bored my friends rigid with tales of this one ... Condition exceptional for a links ... In years to come will be one of the best in Ireland ... A fresh look at links golf.

Ardee Golf Club

Ardee, County Louth
Nearest main town: Ardee

Secretary: Mr K. McCarthy
Tel: 041 53227/56283
Fax: 041 56137

Professional: None.

Playing: Midweek: round £17.00; day £17.00. Weekend: round n/a; day n/a. Handicap certificate required.

Facilities: Bar: None. Food: None.

Comments: Parkland setting provides fair challenge to the average golfer ... Not overly testing, but enjoyable ... Nice setting but nothing as a test of golf ... Trees and a stream are the main hazards ... Good value.

Athy Golf Club ★★

Geraldine, Athy, County Kildare
Nearest main town: Athy

Secretary: Mr B. Watchorn   Tel: 01 507 31729
                   (Hon. Secretary)   Fax: 01 507 32022

Professional: None.

Playing: Midweek: round IR£13.00; day n/a. Weekend: round
                   IR£12.00 (with Member only); day n/a. Handicap certifi-
                   cate required.

Facilities: Bar: 10am–11pm daily. Food: Food is available on
                   request.

Comments: Opened in 1993, this parkland course has many inter-
                   esting golf holes ... The long 16th has a deep 'valley of
                   sin' to the right whilst the unique dogleg 17th plays
                   downhill to a two-tier elevated green.

Balbriggan Golf Course   ★

Blackhall, Balbriggan, County Dublin
Nearest main town: Balbriggan

Secretary: Mr M. O'Halloran   Tel: 01 841 2229
                   (Secretary/Manager)   Fax: 01 841 3927

Professional: None.

Playing: Midweek: round £18.00 Mon, Wed, Thu, Fri (£10.00
                   early bird to 10am; day n/a. Weekend: round with
                   Member only; day n/a. Handicap certificate required.

Facilities: Bar: 11am–11.30pm. Food: Full catering available.

Comments: A rolling parkland course with good views of the east
                   coast and Mourne and Cooley mountains ... Located
                   near Dublin just off the Dublin–Belfast motorway.

Balcarrick Golf Club

Corballis, Donabate, County Dublin
Nearest main town: Donabate

Secretary: Ms J. Byrne   Tel: 01 843 6228
                                          Fax: 01 843 6957

Professional: None.

Playing: Midweek: round £13.00; day £20.00. Weekend: round
                   n/a; day n/a. Handicap certificate required.

Facilities: Bar: None. Food: None.

Comments: A relatively new club, founded in 1992 with many feature holes ... The par-5 8th is a fine dogleg with scenic views across the bay of Malahide ... Good clubhouse facilities.

Beaverstown Golf Club

Donabate, Swords, County Dublin
Nearest main town: Swords

Secretary: Mr F. Ward   Tel: 01 843 6439
                                      Fax: 01 843 6721
Professional: None.

Playing: Midweek: round £20.00; day n/a. Weekend: round £25.00; day n/a. Handicap certificate required.

Facilities: Bar: Usual opening hours apply. Food: Full service.

Comments: This Eddie Hackett layout near The Island was originally a fruit farm ... Acres of apple trees blossom in May ... Water comes into play on ten holes in this attractive orchard setting.

Beech Park Golf Club

Johnstown, Rathcoole, County Dublin
Nearest main town: Dublin

Secretary: Mr J. Deally   Tel: 01 458 0522/458 0100
                                      Fax: 01 458 8365
Professional: None.

Playing: Midweek: round £22.00; day n/a. Weekend: round n/a; day n/a. Handicap certificate required.

Facilities: Bar: None. Food: None.

Comments: Built in 1983 on attractive undulating land, the course is picturesque with, as the name suggests, an abundance of mature trees ... A well positioned lake ensures a 'watery dual' at the 11th, 12th and 13th holes.

The Black Bush Golf Club   ★★

Thomastown, Dunshaughlin, County Meath
Nearest main town: Dublin

Secretary: Mr M. Walsh   Tel: 01 825 0021
                    (Manager)   Fax: 01 825 0400
Professional: Mr S. O'Grady   Tel: 01 825 0793

Playing: Midweek: round £16.00; day n/a. Weekend: round
                    £22.00; day n/a. Handicap certificate required.

Facilities: Bar: 10.30am–11pm. Food: Lunch and dinner from
                    10am–9pm. Bar snacks.

Comments: A young club with great potential – very friendly ...
                    Exciting 1st with drive over the lake ... Superb facilities
                    ... Par-4s cater for average player ... Plenty of short
                    par-4s.

Bodenstown Golf Club   ★★★

Bodenstown, Sallins, County Kildare
Nearest main town: Sallins, 18 miles west of Dublin

Secretary: Mr J. Sexton   Tel: 045 97096
Professional: None.

Playing: Midweek: round £12.00 Old Course, Visitors not allowed
                    at weekend, £10.00 Ladyhill Course; day n/a. Weekend:
                    round n/a; day n/a. Handicap certificate required.

Facilities: Bar: None. Food: None.

Comments: The Old Course at Bodenstown with its ample fairways
                    and large greens, some of which are raised, provides
                    one of the finest inland tests of golf in Leinster ... The
                    Ladyhill course is a little shorter but still affords a worthy
                    challenge ... Popular with Irish golfers.

Carlow Golf Club   ★★★

Deer Park, Dublin Road, Carlow, County Carlow
Nearest main town: Carlow

Secretary: Mrs M. Meaney   Tel: 0503 31695
                                         Fax: 0503 40065
Professional: Mr A. Gilbert   Tel: 0503 41745

Playing: Midweek: round £22.00; day n/a. Weekend: round
                    £27.00; day n/a. Handicap certificate required.

Facilities: Bar: 9.30am–11pm. Food: Breakfast, lunch and dinner
                    from 9.30am–10pm. Bar snacks.

Comments: 16th and 17th are outstanding holes ... Always on my list to play ... Parkland with the best greens in Ireland ... Excellent value with panoramic view from the 8th tee ... All the challenges laid out fairly in front of you ... Well-thought-out layout with subtle protection to good scoring – liked it a lot.

Castle Golf Club   ★★

Woodside Drive, Rathgarnham, Dublin 14, County Dublin
Nearest main town: Dublin

Secretary: Mr L. Blackburne   Tel: 01 492 0264
Professional: Mr D. Kinsella   Tel: 01 492 0272

Playing: Midweek: round £37; day n/a. Weekend: round n/a; day n/a. Handicap certificate required.

Facilities: Bar: 11am–11.30pm. Food: A la Carte and Snack menus.

Comments: Designed by Henry Colt, this undulating south-side course has wonderful views of the Dublin Mountains ... Noted for very tight fairways especially at the signature hole – the index 1, dogleg 6th.

Castle Barna Golf Club   ★★

Castlebarnagh, Daingean, County Offaly
Nearest main town: Toolmaker 12 miles

Secretary: Mr E. Mangan   Tel: 050 653384
Professional: None.

Playing: Midweek: round £8.00; day £10.00. Weekend: round n/a; day n/a. Handicap certificate required.

Facilities: Bar: None. Food: None.

Comments: Peaceful and inexpensive parkland course in the heart of Ireland ... Built on the banks of the Grand Canal with lots of mature trees and natural streams.

Castle Comer Golf Club   ★★

Castle Comer, County Kilkenny
Nearest main town: Castle Comer

Secretary: Mr M. Dooley   Tel: 056 41139
                                          Fax: 056 41139
Professional: None.

Playing: Midweek: round £12.00; day £12.00. Weekend: round
                   n/a; day n/a. Handicap certificate required.

Facilities: Bar: 12.30–11pm. Food: As required for groups.

Comments: An interesting Pat Ruddy design in a sylvan setting by the
                   River Deen ... One of the longest and most testing 9-
                   holers in Ireland ... Friendly atmosphere.

Castlewarden Golf & Country Club   ★

Straffan, County Kildare
Nearest main town: Dublin

Secretary: Mr J. Ferriter   Tel: 01 458 9254
                                          Fax: 01 458 8972
Professional: Mr G. Egan   Tel: 01 458 8219

Playing: Midweek: round £20.00; day n/a. Weekend: round
                   £20.00; day n/a. Handicap certificate required.

Facilities: Bar: 10.30am–11pm. Food: Lunch and dinner from
                   noon–9pm.

Comments: New course with views of the Wicklow mountains ...
                   Under ten years old with the best yet to come ... Nice
                   welcome at this attractive, basic course.

Charlesland Golf Club   ★★★

Greystones, County Wicklow
Nearest main town: Dublin

Secretary: Mr L. Evans   Tel: 01 287 4350
                   (Golf Centre Manager) Fax: 01 287 4360
Professional: Mr P. Heeney

Playing: Midweek: round £26.00; day £40.00. Weekend: round
                   £33.00; day £50.00. Handicap certificate required.

Facilities: Bar: 10.30am–11pm. Food: Bar snacks.

Comments: Water hazards form course defence ... Not overly
                   impressed ... Setting can't be faulted ... Best views from
                   the 13th ... Located in the shadow of Sugarloaf
                   Mountain ... Club with friendly attitude.

Cill Dara Golf Club ★★

Little Curragh, Kildare, County Kildare
Nearest main town: Kildare

Secretary:	Mr P. Flanagan	Tel: 045 521433/52195
Professional:	Mr M. O'Boyle	

Playing: Midweek: round £10.00; day £12.00. Weekend: round n/a; day n/a. Handicap certificate required.

Facilities: Bar: None. Food: None.

Comments: Located beside the Curragh racecourse, near to Kildare town ... Cill Dara is a 9-hole course with gorse and heather featuring on many holes.

Citywest Golf Club ★★

Saggart, Dublin, County Dublin
Nearest main town: Dublin 10 miles

Secretary:	Mr B. Cooling	Tel: 01 458 8566
		Fax: 01 831 5779
Professional:	None.	

Playing: Midweek: round £29.00; day £32.00. Weekend: round n/a; day n/a. Handicap certificate required.

Facilities: Bar: None. Food: None.

Comments: A delightful little course, not too far from Dublin, making it accessible to the weekend visitor ... Check availability of tee times ... At 6441 yards, it makes for a decent day's golf.

Clontarf Golf Club ★

Donnycarney House, Dublin, County Dublin
Nearest main town: Dublin

Secretary:	Mr A. Hall	Tel: 01 833 1892
		Fax: 01 833 1933
Professional:	Mr J. Craddock	Tel: 01 833 1877

Playing: Midweek: round £26.00; day n/a. Weekend: round £35.00; day n/a. Handicap certificate required.

Facilities: Bar: 10.30am–11pm. Food: Bar snacks.

Comments: Parkland course in Dublin suburbs ... Nearest course to
Dublin ... In poor condition ... A little over-used ...
Clubhouse the star ... 12th played over a quarry ...
Watch out for the trains rattling by.

Coldwinters Golf Club   ★★

Newton House, St Margarets, County Dublin
Nearest main town: Dublin 6 miles, Swords 3.5 miles

Secretary: Mr G. Beattie   Tel: 01 864 0324
                                               Fax: 01 834 1400
Professional: Mr R. Machin   Tel: 01 854 0324
                  (Coldwinters Golf Club)   Fax: 01 834 1400

Playing: Midweek: round £10.00; day n/a. Weekend: round
£15.00; day n/a. Handicap certificate required.

Facilities: Bar: n/a. Food: Soup and sandwiches, snacks, etc.

Comments: Comparatively new course but now starting to look more
mature ... Located only a couple of miles from Dublin
Airport ... Full 18 holes plus a 9-hole course ... With a
driving range and Golf Academy, this is a good place to
brush up your swing ... Not a great course but good
value for money.

Corrstown Golf Club   ★★

Corrstown, Kilsallaghan, County Dublin
Nearest main town: Swords

Secretary: Mr J. Kelly   Tel: 01 864 0533
                                               Fax: 01 864 0537
Professional: Mr P. Gittens   Tel: 01 864 3322

Playing: Midweek: round £20.00; day n/a. Weekend: round
£25.00 (only afternoon); day n/a. Handicap certificate
required.

Facilities: Bar: 10.30am–11.30pm. Food: During bar hours.

Comments: Designed by Eddie Cannoughton, the championship
'River Course' clearly reflects the mind of an accom-
plished golfer in tune with nature ... The closing hole
requires a daunting approach to an island green ...
Great value golf.

County Longford Golf Club ★★

Glack, Dublin Road, Longford, County Longford
Nearest main town: Longford

Secretary:	Mr E. Dooley	Tel: 01 434 6310
	(Hon. Secretary)	Fax: 01 434 7082
		e-mail: colongolf@eircom.NET

Professional: None.

Playing: Midweek: round £12.00 without Member, £10.00 with Member; day n/a. Weekend: round £15.00 without Member, £13.00 with Member; day n/a. Handicap certificate required.

Facilities: Bar: Variable according to season. Food: Food available on request.

Comments: An elevated parkland course, overlooking Longford town and surrounding countryside ... Remodelled in the 1970s.

County Louth Golf Club ★★★★

Baltray, Drogheda, County Louth
Nearest main town: Drogheda

Secretary:	Mr M. Delany	Tel: 041 9822327
		Fax: 041 9822969
Professional:	Mr P. McGuirk	Tel: 041 982444

Playing: Midweek: round £45.00; day £45.00. Weekend: round £55.00; day £55.00. Handicap certificate required.

Facilities: Bar: 10.30am–11pm. Food: Lunch and dinner from 10am–9pm. Bar snacks.

Comments: One of the best in Ireland ... Classic and very enjoyable ... Food always good ... A refined course, not as wild as some other renowned courses ... Difficult to get on due to competitions.

Courtown Golf Club ★★★

Kiltennel, Gorey, County Wexford
Nearest main town: Gorey

Secretary:	Mr D. Cleery	Tel: 055 25166
		Fax: 055 25553

Professional: Mr J. Coone   Tel: 055 25166

Playing: Midweek: round £18.00; day n/a. Weekend: round £23.00; day n/a. Handicap certificate required.

Facilities: Bar: 10.30am–11pm. Food: Lunch and dinner from 10am–9pm.

Comments: Friendly, quality golf ... Venue for learners ... Very few doglegs ... Nice alternative to nearby 'super courses' like the European ... Cheap and cheerful holiday golf ... Needs toughening up ... Parkland course that deserves praise.

Deer Park Golf Club ★★

Deer Park Hotel, Howth, County Dublin
Nearest main town: Dublin

Secretary: Mr J . Doran   Tel: 01 8322624
                                     Fax: 01 8392405

Professional: None.

Playing: Midweek: round £9.40; day n/a. Weekend: round £11.50; day n/a. Handicap certificate required.

Facilities: Bar: 10.30am–11pm. Food: Breakfast, lunch and dinner from 7am–10pm. Bar snacks.

Comments: Huge golf complex with fine facilities ... Great value ... A kind of hypermarket for all your golfing needs ... Subtle course ... Very busy course – was it worth the effort? ... Don't listen to the snobs, this is a great facility for the high-handicapper ... Boasts itself as Ireland's largest golf complex ... Nice views from fairways of so-so course.

Delvin Castle Golf Club ★

Clonyn, Delvin, County Westmeath
Nearest main town: Mullingar

Secretary: Mr P. Murphy   Tel: 044 64315
Professional: Mr D. Keenaghan
Playing: Midweek: round £14.00; day n/a. Weekend: round £16.00; day n/a. Handicap certificate required.

Facilities: Bar: 10.30am–11pm. Food: Bar snacks.

Comments: Basic course near Clonyn Castle ... Unmemorable ... Suitable for beginners ... New facility for beginners but not for those seeking new experiences ... New club that tries hard.

Donabate Golf Club ★★★

Balcarrick, Donabate, County Dublin
Nearest main town: Dublin 10 miles

Secretary: Mr B. Judd   Tel: 01 843 6346/6059/6001
                                     Fax: 01 843 5012

Professional: Mr H. Jackson

Playing: Midweek: round £20.00; day n/a. Weekend: round n/a; day n/a. Handicap certificate required.

Facilities: Bar: None. Food: None.

Comments: At 6187 yards, and par 69, this course can be a bit gruelling for the long player ... Just north of Dublin Airport, this is a good course for the weekend traveller.

Druid's Glen Golf Club ★★★★

Newtownmountkennedy, Greystones, County Wicklow
Nearest main town: Newtownmountkennedy

Secretary: Mr D. Flinn   Tel: 01 287 3600
                                     Fax: 01 287 3699

Professional: Mr E. Darcy

Playing: Midweek: round £80.00; day n/a. Weekend: round £80.00; day n/a. Handicap certificate required.

Facilities: Bar: 11am–11pm. Food: Breakfast, lunch and dinner from 9am–11pm. Bar snacks.

Comments: Complete luxury ... Like Mount Juliet for comfort, but course not as good ... Too expensive and exclusive ... Doesn't feel like Irish golf ... Generous fairways and greens – too easy ... Condition first class ... Never seen fairways and greens so good ... Watch out for Amen Corner.

Dun Laoghaire Golf Club ★★★

Eglinton Park, Tivoli Road, Dun Laoghaire, County Dublin
Nearest main town: Dun Laoghaire/Dublin

Secretary:	Mr D. Peacock	Tel: 01 280 3916
		Fax: 01 280 4868
Professional:	Mr O. Mulhall	Tel: 01 280 4868

Playing: Midweek: round £30.00; day n/a. Weekend: round £30.00; day n/a. Handicap certificate required.

Facilities: Bar: 11am–11pm. Food: Available seven days a week.

Comments: First founded 1910, the course was redesigned by the famous Harry Colt, who also designed outstanding British courses, such as Sunningdale ... Enjoyable parkland layout that's reasonably testing but not too demanding ... Quite short but what it lacks in length it more than makes up for in design ... High premium on correct club selection.

Dundalk Golf Club ★★★

Blackrock, Dundalk, County Louth
Nearest main town: Dundalk

Secretary:	Mr J. Carroll	Tel: 042 21731
		Fax: 042 22022
Professional:	Mr J. Cassidy	Tel: 042 22102

Playing: Midweek: round £19.50; day n/a. Weekend: round £23.50; day n/a. Handicap certificate required.

Facilities: Bar: 10.30am–11pm. Food: Lunch and dinner from noon–9pm. Bar snacks.

Comments: Not as good as nearby County Down but a cracker ... Mountains of Mourne form a marvellous canvas for shots ... Forget the bump-and-run of nearby County Down, you need to hit them high here ... Get to the turn in good shape and you should score well ... Nice welcome ... This and Greenore give excellent, good value golf.

Edmondstown Golf Club ★

Rathfarnham, Dublin, County Dublin
Nearest main town: Dublin

Secretary:	Mr S. Davies	Tel: 01 493 1082
		Fax: 01 493 3152
Professional:	Mr A. Crofton	Tel: 01 494 1049

Playing: Midweek: round £25.00; day n/a. Weekend: round £30.00; day n/a. Handicap certificate required.

Facilities: Bar: 10.30am–11pm. Food: Lunch and dinner from noon–9pm. Bar snacks.

Comments: Nothing special about this parkland course ... Overpriced ... Pleasant enough ... Convenient if you're staying in Dublin ... Better courses to be found nearby.

Enniscorthy Golf Club ★★

Knockmarshall, Enniscorthy, County Wexford
Nearest main town: Enniscorthy

Secretary:	Mr B. Kenny	Tel: 054 33191
		Fax: 054 37637
Professional:	Mr M. Sludds	Tel: 054 376000

Playing: Midweek: round £15.00; day £18.00 (1998). Weekend: round n/a; day n/a. Handicap certificate required.

Facilities: Bar: None. Food: None.

Comments: Mature parkland layout designed by one of Ireland's best known architects, Eddie Hackett ... Redesigned and upgraded in recent years ... Very welcoming to visitors.

Forrest Little Golf Club ★★

Cloghran, Swords, County Dublin
Nearest main town: Swords

Secretary:	Mr T. Greany	Tel: 01 840 1763
		Fax: 01 840 1000
Professional:	Mr T. Judd	Tel: 01 840 7670

Playing: Midweek: round £25.00; day n/a. Weekend: round n/a; day n/a. Handicap certificate required.

Facilities: Bar: 11am–midnight. Food: 10am–9pm.

Comments: Top quality layout ... Can be a little noisy at times when the planes are taking off from nearby Dublin Airport ... Look out for the stream that meanders through the course and comes into play on several holes ... Good quality fairways and greens, not surprised to learn the course is a pre-qualifying venue for the Irish Open.

Glasson Golf & Country Club   ★★★★

Glasson, Athlone, County Westmeath
Nearest main town: Athlone

Secretary: Mrs F. Reed   Tel: 090 285120
                                            Fax: 090 285444

Professional: None.

Playing: Midweek: round £27.00; day n/a. Weekend: round £32.00; day n/a. Handicap certificate required.

Facilities: Bar: 10.30am–11pm. Food: Breakfast, lunch and dinner from 9am–9pm. Bar snacks.

Comments: Most enjoyable ... Remarkable location ... Great addition to Ireland's courses ... A little hilly but scenery takes your mind off it ... Worth the drive ... Situated on a peninsula bordering Lough Ree – magnificent ... What do you expect from Christy O'Connor Jr? ... The course on everyone's lips ... Tee and green situated in a lake at the 15th.

Greenore Golf Club   ★★

Greenore, County Louth
Nearest main town: Dundalk

Secretary: Mrs R. Daly   Tel: 042 73212
                                            Fax: 042 73678

Professional: None.

Playing: Midweek: round £14.00; day n/a. Weekend: round £20.00; day n/a. Handicap certificate required.

Facilities: Bar: 10.30am–11pm. Food: Lunch and dinner from noon–9pm. Bar snacks.

Comments: Part links, part woodland ... Variety in buckets – links, woods, a railway line and blind greens ... A new challenge at every turn ... Had a ball ... Will go back as soon as possible.

Headfort Golf Club   ★★★

Kells, County Meath
Nearest main town: Dublin

Secretary: Mrs E. Carroll   Tel: 046 40146
                                       Fax: 046 49282
Professional: Mr B. McGovern   Tel: 046 40639

Playing: Midweek: round £18.00; day n/a. Weekend: round £22.00; day n/a. Handicap certificate required.

Facilities: Bar: 10.30am–11pm. Food: Lunch and dinner from 10am–9pm. Bar snacks.

Comments: Beautiful parkland, hundreds of mature trees ... Value ... Excellent greens and fairways ... Excellent parkland course ... Greens fast and fair ... Easy to get a game, never overcrowded ... One of the top parkland courses in Ireland.

Hermitage Golf Club   ★★★

Lucan, County Dublin
Nearest main town: Dublin

Secretary: Mr T. Stelman   Tel: 01 626 8491
              (Manager)   Fax: 01 626 8491
Professional: Mr S. Burn   Tel: 01 626 8072

Playing: Midweek: round £32.00; day n/a. Weekend: round n/a; day n/a. Handicap certificate required.

Facilities: Bar: 10.30am–11pm. Food: Lunch and dinner from 12.30pm–9pm. Bar snacks.

Comments: Nicely laid out, in good condition with good facilities ... Pretty inland course with unusual features ... Run-of-the-mill parkland track ... A few steep climbs ... Patience required with a few blind shots ... 10th a fine par-3 ... Seemingly simple course but danger lurks everywhere.

Hollywood Lakes Golf Club   ★★

Ballyboughal, Ballyboughal, County Dublin
Nearest main town: Dublin

Secretary:	Mr A. Brogan	Tel: 01 843 3406
		Fax: 01 843 3002
Professional:	None.	

Playing: Midweek: round n/a; day n/a. Weekend: round n/a; day n/a. Handicap certificate required.

Facilities: Bar: 11am–11pm. Food: Lunch from noon–4pm. Dinner by arrangement.

Comments: Green fees on application ... Very long parkland course built to high specifications ... Modern course with water everywhere ... Fun course with water and 600+ yard par-5 ... Dreary new design ... Average condition for new course ... Modern club with fair facilities.

The K Club   ★★★★

Kildare Hotel & Country Club, Straffan,
Nearest main town: Dublin

Secretary:	Mr P. Crowe	Tel: 01 601 7300
		Fax: 01 601 7399
Professional:	Mr E. Jones	Tel: 01 601 7321

Playing: Midweek: round £130.00; day n/a. Weekend: round £130.00; day n/a. Handicap certificate required.

Facilities: Bar: 10.30am–11pm. Food: Breakfast, lunch and dinner from 7am–10pm. Bar snacks.

Comments: Ideal Ryder Cup venue – superb ... Four hours of my life I'll never get back – dreadful ... I don't reckon Arnie would finish this long, punishing track ... Thinking man's course ... Superb ... Good if you are good, a nightmare if you are bad ... High-class professional approach here ... Fantastic condition ... No expense spared here.

Kilkea Castle Golf Club   ★

Carlow, Castle Dermot, County Kildare
Nearest main town: Carlow

Secretary: Mrs K. Nolan   Tel: 050 345156
                                          Fax: 050 345505
Professional: None.

Playing: Midweek: round £25.00; day n/a. Weekend: round
                    £25.00; day n/a. Handicap certificate required.

Facilities: Bar: 10.30am–11pm. Food: Lunch from noon–2pm.
                    Dinner from 6pm–9pm.

Comments: Twelfth-century castle dominates this magical parkland
                    course ... Natural and in immaculate condition on visit
                    ... Clubhouse a perfect 19th ... Course does not match
                    the opulence of the surroundings ... Two man-made
                    lakes and stream are primary defence of this layout.

Kilkenny Golf Club

Glendine, Kilkenny, County Kilkenny
Nearest main town: Kilkenny

Secretary: Mr S. O'Neill   Tel: 056 65400
                                          Fax: 056 23593
Professional: Mr N. Leahy   Tel: 056 61730

Playing: Midweek: round £20.00; day n/a. Weekend: round
                    £25.00; day n/a. Handicap certificate required.

Facilities: Bar: 11am onwards. Food: Available during Bar hours
                    and on request.

Comments: Championship-quality course ... Superb layout set in
                    some 120 acres of mature, lush parkland ... Good
                    enough to have hosted the Carrol's Irish Matchplay
                    Championship ... Although the terrain is pretty flat and
                    easy to walk there are plenty of trees just waiting to
                    swallow up any wayward shots.

Killeen Golf Club

Killeenbeg, Kill, County Kildare
Nearest main town: Sallins

Secretary: Mr P. Carey   Tel: 045 866003
                                          Fax: 045 875881
Professional: None.

Playing: Midweek: round £17.00; day n/a. Weekend: round
                    £20.00; day n/a. Handicap certificate required.

Facilities: Bar: 10.30am–11pm. Food: Lunch and dinner from 10am–9pm. Bar snacks.

Comments: Tight driving course, a pleasure to walk and play ... Short course, fairly tight ... Some holes designed around lakes ... Little of interest at this parkland venue.

Killiney Golf Club ★★

Ballinclea Road, Killiney, County Dublin
Nearest main town: Dublin 8 miles

Secretary: Mr M. O'Rourke   Tel: 01 285 2823
Fax: 01 285 2823

Professional: Mr P. O'Boyle   Tel: 01 285 6294

Playing: Midweek: round £20.00; day n/a. Weekend: round n/a; day n/a. Handicap certificate required.

Facilities: Bar: None. Food: None.

Comments: Very pleasant parkland course ... Excellent condition ... Well established 9-hole course played from outward and inward tees.

Knockanally Golf Club ★★

Donadea, North Kildare, County Kildare
Nearest main town: Dublin

Secretary: Mr N. Lyons   Tel: 045 869322
Fax: 045 869322

Professional: Mr M. Darcy

Playing: Midweek: round £20.00; day n/a. Weekend: round £25.00; day n/a. Handicap certificate required.

Facilities: Bar: 10.30am–11pm. Food: Bar snacks. Dinner by arrangement.

Comments: One of the toughest opening holes in all of golf ... Clubhouse magnificent ... Undulating course that tails off after the opening hole ... Popular parkland course, can get busy.

Lucan Golf Course ★★

Celbridge Road, Lucan, County Dublin
Nearest main town: Lucan

Secretary: Mr T. O'Donnell   Tel: 01 628 2106
                                            Fax: 01 628 2929
Professional: None.

Playing: Midweek: round £25.00; day n/a. Weekend: round n/a;
                    day n/a. Handicap certificate required.

Facilities: Bar: 11am–11.30pm. Food: Bar snacks and full cater-
                    ing available.

Comments: Short but interesting to play ... You will enjoy the experi-
                    ence of playing the par-3 4th hole, where the tee shot is
                    played across a main road ... Pleasant, if undemanding
                    parkland layout.

Luttrellstown Castle Golf Club ★★★

Clonsilla, Clonsilla, County Dublin
Nearest main town: Dublin

Secretary: Mr J. McColgan   Tel: 01 808 9988
                    (Manager)   Fax: 01 808 9989
Professional: Mr G. Campbell

Playing: Midweek: round £40.00; day n/a. Weekend: round
                    £45.00; day n/a. Handicap certificate required.

Facilities: Bar: 10.30am–11pm. Food: Lunch and dinner from
                    noon–9pm. Bar snacks.

Comments: Excellent fairways and greens on a well-designed, tough-
                    but-fair course ... Beautiful and challenging ... The day
                    I win the lotto is the day I join this great course ...
                    Excellent clubhouse and brilliant food ... Lots of water
                    fun, not so good for the traditionalist ... Always find time
                    to play it ... One of the best newer courses in Ireland.

Malahide Golf Club ★★

Beechwood, The Grange, Malahide, County Dublin
Nearest main town: Dublin

Secretary:	Mr T. Gallagher	Tel: 01 846 1611
		Fax: 01 846 1270
Professional:	Mr D. Barton	Tel: 01 846 0002

Playing: Midweek: round £30.00; day n/a. Weekend: round £40.00; day n/a. Handicap certificate required.

Facilities: Bar: 10.30am–11pm. Food: Lunch and dinner from 11am–9pm. Bar snacks.

Comments: Very popular, friendly course ... Not a classic design but kept in excellent shape ... For all the challenge from the tee and fairway, the greens are generally flat ... Very fair to the once-in-a-while player ... Scoring usually good here ... Facilities excellent at this popular Dublin parkland course ... Clever use of water hazards.

Milltown Golf Club ★★

Lower Churchtown Road, Milltown, Dublin 14, County Dublin
Nearest main town: Dublin 4 miles

Secretary:	Mr D. Dalton	Tel: 01 497 6090
		Fax: 01 497 6008
Professional:	Mr J. Harnett	Tel: 01 497 7072

Playing: Midweek: round IR£35; day Booking preferable. Weekend: round n/a; day n/a. Handicap certificate required.

Facilities: Bar: None. Food: None.

Comments: Very attractive and well kept golf course ... Fairly flat but enjoyable parkland layout ... Fairly short but a good test nevertheless ... Well established golf course in a pleasant setting ... Friendly welcome with extensive clubhouse facilities.

Mount Temple Golf Club ★★★

Mount Temple, Moate, County Westmeath
Nearest main town: Moate

Secretary:	Mr M. Dolan	Tel: 0902 81841
		Fax: 0902 81957
Professional:	None.	

Playing: Midweek: round £15.00; day n/a. Weekend: round £18.00; day n/a. Handicap certificate required.

Facilities: Bar: None. Food: Bar snacks.

Comments: It's a beast but worth the pain ... Long and difficult course ... Extremely natural layout ... Undulating fairways and hard, unwatered greens make this a test of your imagination ... Shot-maker's course.

Mount Wolsley Golf Club

Tullow, County Carlow
Nearest main town: Tullow

Secretary: Mr D. Morrissey   Tel: 0503 51674
                                   Fax: 0503 52123

Professional: Mr J. Bolger

Playing: Midweek: round £20.00; day n/a. Weekend: round £25.00; day n/a. Handicap certificate required.

Facilities: Bar: 11am–11pm. Food: Lunch and dinner from 11am–10pm. Bar snacks.

Comments: Very fun course ... New course in super condition ... A dream to play ... Can't wait to go back.

Mountrath Golf Club ★

Knockanina, County Laois
Nearest main town: Portlaoise

Secretary: Mr J. Mulhare   Tel: 0502 32558
                                 Fax: 0502 32558

Professional: None.

Playing: Midweek: round £10.00; day n/a. Weekend: round £10.00; day n/a. Handicap certificate required.

Facilities: Bar: 10.30am–11pm. Food: Bar snacks.

Comments: Sheep the main hazard on this 9-hole course ... Fun course open to everyone ... A beginner's course.

Mullingar Golf Club

Belvedere, Mullingar, County Westmeath
Nearest main town: Mullingar

Secretary:	Mrs A. Cully	Tel: 044 48366
		Fax: 044 41499
Professional:	Mr J. Burns	Tel: 044 40085

Playing: Midweek: round £20.00; day n/a. Weekend: round £25.00; day n/a. Handicap certificate required.

Facilities: Bar: 10.30am–11pm. Food: Lunch and dinner from noon–9pm. Bar snacks.

Comments: Tactical short course ... Despite being less than 6000 yards, this course has stood the test of time ... Tight course ... Greens cleverly protected ... Bunkering protects this short course ... Will remember it for the par-3s ... Always a warm welcome.

Old Conna Golf Club ★

Ferndale Road, Bray, County Wicklow
Nearest main town: Dublin

Secretary:	Mr D. Diviney	Tel: 01 282 6055
		Fax: 01 282 5611
Professional:	Mr P. McDaid	Tel: 01 272 0022

Playing: Midweek: round £27.50; day n/a. Weekend: round n/a; day n/a. Handicap certificate required.

Facilities: Bar: 10.30am–11pm. Food: Lunch and dinner from 10am–9pm. Bar snacks.

Comments: New course near Dublin that has a bright future ... Time will tell whether this Hackett course will make it ... Three of the last four holes are 420+ yards ... Overly long new course ... New players don't need to cover 6000+ yards.

Open Golf Centre, Home of Coldwinters Golf Club ★

Newton House, St Margarets, County Dublin
Nearest main town: Dublin 6 miles, Swords 3.5 miles

Secretary:	Mr G. Beattie	Tel: 01 864 0324
		Fax: 01 834 1400
Professional:	Mr R. Yates	Tel: 01 854 0324
	(Open Golf Centre)	Fax: 01 834 1400

Playing: Midweek: round £10.00; day n/a. Weekend: round £15.00; day n/a. Handicap certificate required.

Facilities: Bar: n/a. Food: Soup and sandwiches, snacks, etc.

Comments: Home of the golf club with its 27 holes, but also has the biggest pro shop in Ireland ... Open every day for lessons from 9am–10pm ... Five professionals working here ... Twenty driving bays for practising.

Powerscourt Golf Club ★★★

Enniskerry, Bray, County Wicklow
Nearest main town: Bray

Secretary:	Mr B. Gibbons	Tel: 01 204 6033
Professional:	Mr P. Thompson	Tel: 01 204 6033

Playing: Midweek: round £45.00; day n/a. Weekend: round £55.00; day n/a. Handicap certificate required.

Facilities: Bar: 9am–11pm. Food: Lunch and dinner from noon–9pm.

Comments: Wicklow mountains provide a stunning backdrop ... Dublin golfers are becoming very spoiled ... Par-5 17th of 698 yards not quite what I'm used to ... Inventive course but not much soul ... Felt very welcome ... Condition a tribute to the club.

Rathsallagh Golf Club ★★★★

Dunlavin, Dunlavin, County Wicklow
Nearest main town: Naas

Secretary:	Mr M. Bermingham	Tel: 045 403316
		Fax: 045 403295
Professional:	None.	

Playing: Midweek: round £35.00; day n/a. Weekend: round £45.00; day n/a. Handicap certificate required.

Facilities: Bar: 10.30am–11pm. Food: Lunch and dinner from noon–9pm. Bar snacks.

Comments: Difficult, long course suitable for players of all abilities ... Beautiful setting and good value ... So much variety ... A bit of everything at this Peter McEvoy-designed course ... Watch out for the 6th ... Hard as nails ... Homely club ... Simple from the tee, but the trouble starts when you start firing at the flags.

Rosslare Golf Club ★★★

Rosslare Strand, Rosslare, County Wexford
Nearest main town: Wexford

Secretary:	Mr J. Hall	Tel: 053 32203
		Fax: 053 32203
Professional:	Mr A. Skerritt	Tel: 053 32238

Playing: Midweek: round n/a; day £22.00. Weekend: round n/a; day £30.00. Handicap certificate required.

Facilities: Bar: 10.30am–11pm. Food: Lunch from 10am–9pm. Bar snacks.

Comments: Very pleasant links that lacks length ... Underrated due to its length ... Great welcome at this old-style links ... Very exposed – can spoil the fun ... Rough gets too high on occasions ... Charming little course – will be back.

Royal Dublin Golf Club ★★★★

North Bull Island, Dollymount, Dublin, County Dublin
Nearest main town: Dublin

Secretary:	Mr J. Lambe	Tel: 01 833 1262
		Fax: 01 833 6504
Professional:	Mr L. Owens	Tel: 01 833 6477

Playing: Midweek: round £60.00; day n/a. Weekend: round £70.00; day n/a. Handicap certificate required.

Facilities: Bar: 10.30am–11pm. Food: Breakfast, lunch and dinner from 7am–10pm. Bar snacks.

Comments: Welcome atmosphere ... Superb links and great pro shop ... Past its best ... A stunning natural course with deep greenside bunkers ... Very busy with visitors from Dublin ... Hard-to-master course with blind drives.

Rush Golf Club ★

Rush, County Dublin
Nearest main town: Dublin

Secretary:	Mr B. Clear	Tel: 01 843 7548
		Fax: 01 843 8177
Professional:	None.	

Playing: Midweek: round £16.00; day n/a. Weekend: round n/a; day n/a. Handicap certificate required.

Facilities: Bar: 10.30am–11pm. Food: Bar snacks.

Comments: Nine-hole links with pot bunkers and undulating fairways ... Bunkers the main hazard at his neat little course ... Natural course in average condition ... Excellent fun and a bracing wind ... Good value for a unique golf experience.

Skerries Golf Club   ★★

Skerries,
Nearest main town: Swords or Balbriggan

Secretary: Mr A. Burns   Tel: 01 849 1567
                  (Manager)   Fax: 01 849 1591
Professional: Mr J. Kinsella   Tel: 01 849 0925

Playing: Midweek: round £25.00; day n/a. Weekend: round £30.00; day n/a. Handicap certificate required.

Facilities: Bar: 10am–11.30pm. Food: All day.

Comments: A scenic and popular holiday course with one of the best finishing holes in the country ... Its long par-4 18th winds its way in a semi-dogleg slightly uphill ... Panoramic views from the fine clubhouse.

Slade Valley Golf Club   ★

Lynch Park, Brittas, Dublin, County Dublin
Nearest main town: Dublin 8 miles

Secretary: Mr P. Maguire   Tel: 01 458 2183/2739
                                       Fax: 01 458 2784
Professional: Mr J. Dignam   Tel: 01 458 2739

Playing: Midweek: round £17.00; day n/a. Weekend: round n/a; day n/a. Handicap certificate required.

Facilities: Bar: None. Food: None.

Comments: Not a particularly demanding layout, but the scenery makes for a relaxing game with some interesting holes ... A 'take it easy' course.

St Helens Bay Golf Club ★★

Rosslare Harbour, County Wexford
Nearest main town: Wexford

Secretary: Mr L. Byrne   Tel: 053 33234
                                       Fax: 053 33803
Professional: None.

Playing: Midweek: round £22.00; day n/a. Weekend: round
                    £25.00; day n/a. Handicap certificate required.

Facilities: Bar: 10.30am–11pm. Food: Lunch and dinner from
                    noon–9pm. Bar snacks.

Comments: Part links, part parkland ... Sleeping giant of a course ...
                    Course suffers from identity crisis – is it parkland, is it
                    links? ... Course finishes on right note with some crack-
                    ing closing holes ... Simple course with potential ...
                    Condition leaves a lot to be desired ... Ideal matchplay
                    venue.

St Margarets Golf & Country Club ★★★★

St Margarets, Dublin, County Dublin
Nearest main town: Dublin

Secretary: Mr T. Judge   Tel: 01 864 0400
                    (Chief Executive)   Fax: 01 864 0289
Professional: Mr D. Loys-Moroney

Playing: Midweek: round £30.00; day £45.00. Weekend: round
                    £45.00; day £65.00. Handicap certificate required.

Facilities: Bar: 10.30am–11pm. Food: Breakfast, lunch and
                    dinner from 9am–9pm. Bar snacks.

Comments: Good championship course, but will be outstanding
                    in ten years' time ... Best greens I have ever putted
                    on ... Flat farmland transformed into a rolling, modern
                    masterpiece ... No bump-and-run here, high iron
                    shots needed ... 8th and the 12th are excellent
                    par-5s ... Excellent facilities and course for the average
                    player.

Swords Open Golf Course ★

Balheary Avenue, Swords, County Dublin
Nearest main town: Swords

Secretary: Ms D. McLoughlin Tel: 01 840 9819/1890 1030
(Managing Director) Fax: 01 840 9819
Professional: None.

Playing: Midweek: round £10.00; day n/a. Weekend: round £14.00; day n/a. Handicap certificate required.

Facilities: Bar: Coffee Shop. Food: Soup and sandwiches available.

Comments: Situated in the idyllic surroundings of North County Dublin along the banks of the Broadmeadow river ... It offers a unique golfing experience to every golfer ... Only five minutes from Swords, ten minutes from Dublin Airport and approximately nine miles from the City Centre ... The course is easily accessible and the green fees are very reasonable.

The European Club ★★★★

Brittas Bay, Wicklow, County Wicklow
Nearest main town: Wicklow

Secretary: Mr P. Ruddy Tel: 0404 47415
Fax: 0404 47449
Professional: None.

Playing: Midweek: round £45.00; day £65.00. Weekend: round £45.00; day £65.00. Handicap certificate required.

Facilities: Bar: Wine bar open all day. Food: Breakfast, lunch and dinner from 9am–9pm. Bar snacks.

Comments: Each hole a classic ... Very difficult links ... What a place! ... Easy to get a game on a beautiful links ... Outstanding welcome, manager even joined us for lunch ... Very demanding and exciting ... 7th and 17th are great holes ... Tough course with excellent greens ... Wonderful charm and hospitality.

The Heath Golf Club ★

The Heath, Portlaoise, County Laois
Nearest main town: Portlaoise

Secretary: To be appointed. Tel: 0502 21074
Professional: Mr E. Doyle Tel: 0502 46622

Playing: Midweek: round £10.00; day n/a. Weekend: round £15.00; day n/a. Handicap certificate required.

Facilities: Bar: 10.30am–11pm. Food: Lunch and dinner from noon–6pm.

Comments: Heather and gorse the main feature of this old course ... Old course a little ragged around the edges ... Very natural but very average.

The Island Golf Club   ★★★★

Corballis, Donabate, County Dublin
Nearest main town: Dublin

Secretary: Mr J. Finn   Tel: 01 843 6104
                                      Fax: 01 843 6860
Professional: Mr K. Kelleher   Tel: 01 843 5002

Playing: Midweek: round £40.00; day £60.00. Weekend: round £50.00; day n/a. Handicap certificate required.

Facilities: Bar: 10.30am–11pm. Food: Lunch and dinner from 10am–9pm.

Comments: Good all-round facilities with best holes the 5th, 6th, 10th and 15th ... True links ... Best course in Dublin but needs to be more welcoming ... 1st, 3rd and the 7th are the best holes on the front nine ... Surrounded on three sides by water ... Imposing sandhills in places.

Tullamore Golf Club   ★★★

Brookfield, Tullamore, County Offaly
Nearest main town: Toolmaker

Secretary: Mr P. Burns   Tel: 0506 21439
                                       Fax: 0506 41806
Professional: Mr D. McArdle   Tel: 0506 51757

Playing: Midweek: round £16.00; day £24.00. Weekend: round £20.00; day £30.00. Handicap certificate required.

Facilities: Bar: 10.30am–11pm. Food: Lunch and dinner from 11am–9pm.

Comments: Pure golf and great 14th hole ... Classic course recently improved ... Generous course where good shots are always rewarded ... Nothing tricky about this warm, friendly club ... Best course for miles around.

Wicklow Golf Club   ★★

Dunbur Road, Wicklow, County Wicklow
Nearest main town: Wicklow

Secretary: Mr J. Kelly   Tel: 0404 67379
Professional: Mr D. Daly   Tel: 0404 66122

Playing: Midweek: round £20.00; day £20.00. Weekend: round
                  £20.00; day £20.00. Handicap certificate required.

Facilities: Bar: 10.30am–11pm. Food: Lunch and dinner from
                  10am–10pm. Bar snacks.

Comments: Beautiful scenery on a thinking man's course ... Views of
                  Wicklow mountains best thing about this place ... Short
                  9-holer that offers little but views ... Wouldn't rush back
                  ... There's better 9-holers elsewhere.

Woodbrook Golf Club   ★★★

Dublin Road, Bray, County Dublin
Nearest main town: Dublin

Secretary: Mr J. Melody   Tel: 01 282 4799
                                           Fax: 01 282 1950
Professional: Mr W. Kinsella

Playing: Midweek: round £45.00; day n/a. Weekend: round
                  £55.00; day n/a. Handicap certificate required.

Facilities: Bar: 10.30am–11pm. Food: Lunch and dinner from
                  11am–9pm. Bar snacks.

Comments: Club prides itself on condition of course ... Not a tradi-
                  tional links but a fun place to play ... 36 out, 36 home
                  – nicely balanced course ... A facile links ideal for
                  beginners ... Don't go out of your way.

Woodenbridge Golf Club   ★★★

Woodenbridge, Arklow, County Wicklow
Nearest main town: Arklow

Secretary: Mr H. Crummy   Tel: 0402 35202
                                           Fax: 0402 35202
Professional: None.

Playing:　　Midweek: round £27.00; day n/a. Weekend: round £35.00; day n/a. Handicap certificate required.

Facilities:　　Bar: 11am–11pm. Food: Lunch from 11am–3pm. Dinner from 6pm–11pm. Bar snacks.

Comments:　　Can get very busy during the weekend ... Delightful course in the spring ... Pretty parkland which is very fair ... Setting and vegetation make this course ... Very popular ... Never have a bad round.

Ulster and Donegal

Ballyliffin Golf Club (Glashedy) ★★★★★

Inishowen, Ballyliffin, County Donegal
Nearest main town: Londonderry

Nick Faldo labelled the Old Course at Ballyliffin as 'the most natural course ever'. You could not say the same about its younger brother, the Glashedy, which, although running through a moonscape of dunes, has been levelled out somewhat to create a fair playing surface. If the work had not been done, and the fairways allowed to keep their sloping, rugged appearance, this would surely be the toughest course in Ireland.

Much like Tralee, Portmarnock Links and The European, Glashedy is a 'new' links course, and is the northernmost course in Ireland, situated near Pollan Bay off Doagh Isle. Designed by Pat Ruddy and Tom Craddock on the landward side of the original links, the Glashedy Links exploits its exalted location to the full. The designers promised the club that they would build one of the world's finest and most adventurous links courses, and although such things are hugely subjective, to some extent they succeeded. It is a vigorous test of golf, the wind running the full range from strong to very strong, and the greenkeepers letting the rough grow. You'll need all the shots to survive here, particularly the low runner that keeps below the level of the dunes. Hit it above them and the wind will send your ball flying in all directions and probably into a scrape or bunker.

There is a tremendous sequence of holes on the back nine starting with the par-5 13th, a hole that they say reminds you of Ballybunion when you look ahead and Turnberry when you look behind because of the dominating presence of Glashedy Rock.

Secretary: Mr K. O'Docherty   Tel: 077 76119
                                  Fax: 077 76672
Professional: None.

Playing: Midweek: round £28.00; day n/a. Weekend: round £33.00; day n/a. Handicap certificate required.

Facilities: Bar: 10.30am–11pm. Food: Lunch and dinner from noon–9pm.

Comments: Great value ... Don't go and play here and miss out on
the Old course ... Everything you need for a challenge
– wind, doglegs, subtle greens, deep bunkers and tangly
rough ... 12th, 13th and 14th just can't be bettered ...
Magnificent new course, thank you Ruddy and Craddock
... New course that feels 100 years old.

Royal County Down Golf Club   ★★★★★

Newcastle, County Down BT33 0AN
Nearest main town: Belfast

Along with Royal Dornoch in the nether reaches of Scotland, Royal
County Down is arguably the finest links never to have held an Open
Championship. Praise for this beautiful links, which is towered over by
the spectacular range of the Mountains of Mourne, has come from far
and wide.

Dai Rees felt it to be second only to Pine Valley as the toughest
course in the world. Tom Watson, as qualified as anyone to comment
on the merits of links courses, having won the Open on five different
ones, commented after his 1989 visit that the first 11 holes were 'the
finest consecutive holes of links golf' he had ever played.

County Down's charm lies in the old-fashioned flavour of both the
terrain and the layout. A few other courses are blessed with a similar
mix of rugged dunes ordained with a colourful blend of purple
heather and yellow flowering gorse, but few combine them to such
dramatic effect.

The fairways and greens are no less than you would expect from a
championship seaside course, but the rough has a delightfully unkempt
appearance which gives the feel of playing golf in the last century. Sea
grasses grow from the lip of the bunkers in such thick tufts that it is better
to land in the traps than to just clear them.

The huge spines of dunes which bisect the course have resulted in
five blind tee shots which naturally are a target of criticism in these days
of laser-measured yardage charts. But at County Down they add to the
drama. Take the 486-yard 9th where, following a blind tee shot, you
walk to the top of the ridge to see the glory of one of golf's most
photographed fairways unfold far below you, with the 2300-foot peak
of Slieve Donard in the distance overseeing proceedings. The short par-
4 16th, driveable with a big blow from a hilltop, has also come in for
criticism, but perhaps the only thing out of place at County Down is the
small lake in the middle of the 17th fairway, which seems unnecessarily
contrived.

Secretary: Mr P. Rolph   Tel: 028 4372 3314
                                          Fax: 028 4372 6281
Professional: Mr K. Whitson   Tel: 028 4372 2419

Playing: Midweek: round £65.00; day £95.00. Weekend: round
                   £75.00; day n/a. Handicap certificate required.

Facilities: Bar: 11am–11pm. Food: Lunch and dinner from
                   noon–3pm. Bar snacks.

Comments: Best course in British Isles ... Deserving of its ultra-
                   challenging reputation ... Inspiring setting ... Friendly,
                   well-informed pro ... The course is a dream and the 9th
                   hole is the pick of the bunch ... Maybe the best course
                   in Ireland ... Not a bad hole here ... Breathtakingly
                   beautiful, but don't take your eyes off the course.

Royal Portrush Golf Club (Dunluce)   ★★★★★

Dunluce Road, Portrush, County Antrim BT56 8JQ
Nearest main town: Portrush

Few approaches to a golf course stir the passions more than the road
to Royal Portrush. Shortly after passing the ruins of Dunluce Castle, you
turn a corner and there, spread before you, is an expanse of crumpled
links, rolling out towards the shimmering sea. In the distance are the
brooding headlands of Inishowen and, on a clear day, you can see the
Scottish landmarks of the Paps of Jura. It is a marvellously evocative
setting.

Royal Portrush held the Open Championship in 1951 (the only
course in Ireland to do so), but as the demands on space for hospitality grew, so its viability as a venue fell. It is certainly a course worthy of
the event, and players walking off the 18th breathe a heavy sigh of satis-
faction after what is an incredibly imaginative experience.

Essentially it is a driving course. The curves of the fairways and
slopes of the terrain are intimidating from the tee and, although there
are very few bunkers, the wind is a constant factor, and the rough is
untamed and unruly, gobbling up any loose shot. The opening holes
run fairly straight away from the clubhouse and it is not until the turn
that the course starts to show its teeth. The holes swing back and forth,
doglegging around dunes and greens backing onto the sea, most spectacularly at the 5th. What strikes you is that, although this is the most
difficult part of the course, there are very few greenside bunkers, the
small putting surfaces protected purely by small hummocks and hills.

The 14th, named Calamity Corner, is Portrush's most famous hole,
a par-3 which is played to an elevated green located on a spine of

rising land. All along the right is a hideous drop into a valley of bushes and scrub and, on the left, dangerous rough clinging to the banks.

Secretary: Miss W. Erskine   Tel: 028 7082 2311
                                          Fax: 028 7082 3139
Professional: Mr D. Stevenson   Tel: 028 7082 3335

Playing: Midweek: round £60.00; day £85.00. Weekend: round £70.00; day £95.00. Handicap certificate required.

Facilities: Bar: 11am–11pm. Food: Lunch from 11am–3pm. Dinner by arrangement.

Comments: Magnificent links ... Great setting ... Grandiose ... Take the Open Championship there as soon as possible ... You need the heart of a lion for this one ... A must-play course with great views and wonderful company ... Must be played ... Gruelling ... Just magic ... An unbelievable experience for the overseas golfer.

Ardglass Golf Club   ★★★

Castle Place, Ardglass, County Down BT30 7TP
Nearest main town: Downpatrick

Secretary: Miss D. Polly   Tel: 028 4484 1219
                                          Fax: 028 4484 1841
Professional: Mr P. Farrell   Tel: 028 4484 1022

Playing: Midweek: round £15.00; day £15.00. Weekend: round £21.00; day n/a. Handicap certificate required.

Facilities: Bar: 11am–11pm. Food: Lunch and dinner from noon–9pm, except Mons.

Comments: A jaw-dropping opening hole, delicious food, most notably the steaks! ... Beautiful track by the sea ... Many blind drives will send you potty ... An historic course ... First four holes perched on the cliffs ... par-3 11th blows your socks off ... Very fair, the test of a great golf course.

Ballybofey & Stranorlar Golf Club

Stranorlar, Ballybofey, County Donegal
Nearest main town: Stranorlar

Secretary: Mr A. Harkin   Tel: 074 31228
Professional: None.

Playing: Midweek: round n/a; day £15.00. Weekend: round n/a; day £15.00. Handicap certificate required.

Facilities: Bar: 11am–11pm. Food: Lunch and dinner from noon–9pm. Bar snacks.

Comments: A gentle, fun course ... Intoxicating atmosphere in the clubhouse ... Impossible to leave bar until after midnight ... Warm welcome guaranteed ... Great welcome ... Parkland course more renowned for its welcome than quality of golf ... Good course with views of the Donegal Hills.

Ballycastle Golf Club ★★★

Cushendall Road, Ballycastle, County Antrim BT64 6QP
Nearest main town: Portrush

Secretary: Mr B. Dillon   Tel: 028 2076 2536
Fax: 028 2076 9909
Professional: Mr I. McLaughlin   Tel: 028 2076 2506

Playing: Midweek: round £18.00; day n/a. Weekend: round £25.00; day n/a. Handicap certificate required.

Facilities: Bar: 11am–11pm. Food: Lunch from noon–2pm. Dinner by arrangement.

Comments: Three courses in one ... Mixed parkland/links ... Great character ... Parts played around ruins of 13th-century friary ... Thoughtful course of some standing.

Ballyclare Golf Club ★★

29 Springvale Road, Ballyclare, Belfast, County Antrim BT39 9JW
Nearest main town: Ballyclare; Belfast 14 miles

Secretary: Mr H. McConnell   Tel: 028 9332 2696
Clubhouse 028 9334 2352
Fax: 028 9332 2696
Professional: None.

Playing: Midweek: round £16.00; day £22.00. Weekend: round n/a; day n/a. Handicap certificate required.

Facilities: Bar: None. Food: None.

Comments: An attractive parkland course with tree-lined fairways and natural water hazards ... The signature hole is the demanding par-4 third where the golfer is faced with out of bounds on one side and a lake and river on the other ... Good value meals.

Ballyliffin Golf Club (Old)   ★★★★

Inishowen, Ballyliffin, County Donegal
Nearest main town: Londonderry

Secretary: Mr K. O'Doherty   Tel: 077 76119
                                 Fax: 077 76672

Professional: None.

Playing: Midweek: round £19.00; day n/a. Weekend: round £22.00; day n/a. Handicap certificate required.

Facilities: Bar: 10.30am–11pm. Food: Lunch and dinner from noon–9pm.

Comments: Natural links course set in magnificent scenery ... Faldo calls it 'the most natural golf course ever' ... Watch out for 'The Tank' ... So beautiful ... Shorter than you would expect but so charming ... Never a flat lie on these fairways ... I do my best thinking out here ... Will never forget my time here ... A haven of tranquillity from the modern world.

Balmoral Golf Club   ★★★

518 Lisburn Road, Belfast, County Belfast BT9 6GX
Nearest main town: Belfast

Secretary: Mr R. McConkey   Tel: 028 9038 1514
                                Fax: 028 9066 6759

Professional: Mr G. Bleakley   Tel: 028 9066 7747

Playing: Midweek: round £20.00; day n/a. Weekend: round £30.00; day n/a. Handicap certificate required.

Facilities: Bar: 11am–11pm. Food: Breakfast, lunch and dinner from 9am–9pm. Bar snacks.

Comments: Good course near Belfast city centre ... Very beautiful ... Relaxed clubhouse ... Excellent greens on visit ... Impressive clubhouse ... Fairly short but with plenty of natural hazards ... Tree-lined course with some potential.

Bangor Golf Club   ★★★

Broadway, Bangor, County Down BT20 4RH
Nearest main town: Bangor

Secretary: Mr D. Ryan   Tel: 028 9127 0922
                                            Fax: 028 9145 3394
Professional: None.

Playing: Midweek: round £20.00; day £30.00. Weekend: round
                    £25.00; day n/a. Handicap certificate required.

Facilities: Bar: 11am–11pm. Food: Bar snacks. Dinner by
                    arrangement.

Comments: Good course for the beginner and more experienced
                    player ... Remote course but fun to play ... Numerous
                    doglegs ... Another James Braid triumph ... Natural
                    golf for the purist.

Blackwood Golf Centre   ★★

150 Crawfordsburn Road, Bangor, County Down BT19 6QL
Nearest main town: Bangor

Secretary: Mr R. Gibson   Tel: 028 9185 2706
Professional: Miss D. Hanna   Tel: 028 9185 2706

Playing: Midweek: round £15.00 Hamilton/£8.00 Temple (18
                    hole par-3 course); day n/a. Weekend: round £20.00
                    Hamilton/£10.00 Temple (18 hole par-3 course); day
                    n/a. Handicap certificate required.

Facilities: Bar: Winter 11am–8pm. Summer noon–7pm. Food:
                    None.

Comments: Excellent 9-hole course in pleasant setting ... Fun to play
                    but still a good challenge for the less accomplished
                    player ... Good condition.

Bright Castle Golf Club   ★★

14 Conianstown Road, Bright, Downpatrick, County Down BT30 8LU
Nearest main town: Downpatrick

Secretary: Mr J. McCaul   Tel: 028 4484 1319
                                            Mobile 0370 922943
Professional: None.

Playing: Midweek: round £10.00; day n/a. Weekend: round £12.00; day n/a. Handicap certificate required.

Facilities: Bar: unlicensed as yet, facilities on way. Food: Snack meals available, also sandwiches etc.

Comments: Five par-5 holes make this course a tough old slog when the conditions are tough and the wind gets up ... Long and in places quite physically demanding ... Built in 1979 this is a comparatively new links course, but is also a fine test of golf. Good 'fry-ups' available.

Bundoran Golf Club   ★★★

Bundoran, County Donegal
Nearest main town: Donegal

Secretary: Mr J. McGagh   Tel: 072 41302
            Fax: 072 42014
Professional: Mr D. Robinson

Playing: Midweek: round £17.00; day £25.00. Weekend: round £20.00; day £30.00. Handicap certificate required.

Facilities: Bar: 10.30am–11pm. Food: Bar snacks.

Comments: Venerable links ... Testing par-3s, especially the 5th ... Very popular venue ... Round went on forever ... Parkland/links ... A nice stop-off but too short ... Holes by the ocean hard to beat ... Basic facilities at this welcoming club.

Cairndhu Golf Club   ★★★

192 Coast Road, Larne, County Antrim BT40 2QC
Nearest main town: Larne

Secretary: Mr N. Moore   Tel: 028 2858 3324
            Fax: 028 2858 3324
Professional: Mr R. Walker   Tel: 028 2858 3417

Playing: Midweek: round £15.00; day £22.50. Weekend: round £24.00; day £36.00. Handicap certificate required.

Facilities: Bar: 11am–11pm. Food: Lunch and dinner from 11am–9pm. Bar snacks.

Comments: Don't be intimidated by the scenery ... Built on the side of a hill ... Views to the Antrim Hills ... 3rd tee-shot is from way up high and has to carry 170 yards ... Small greens make this so tough.

Carrickfergus Golf Club ★

35 North Road, Carrickfergus, County Antrim BT38 8LP
Nearest main town: Belfast

Secretary: Mr B. Lee

Tel: 028 9336 3713
Fax: 028 9336 3023

Professional: To be appointed.

Playing: Midweek: round £14.00; day £14.00. Weekend: round £20.00; day £20.00. Handicap certificate required.

Facilities: Bar: 11am–11pm. Food: Lunch from noon–2.30pm. Dinner from 5pm–8.30pm.

Comments: Opening drive straight over a dam ... Very intimidating opening tee shot ... Basic layout with little for the advanced player ... Lots of parallel fairways make this quite boring.

Castle Hume Golf Club

Castle Hume, Enniskillen, County Fermanagh BT93 7ED
Nearest main town: Enniskillen

Secretary: Mr A. Frazer

Tel: 028 6632 7077
Fax: 028 6632 7076

Professional: Professional services available by prior arrangement

Tel: 028 6632 7077
Fax: 028 6632 7076

Playing: Midweek: round £15.00; day n/a. Weekend: round £20.00; day n/a. Handicap certificate required.

Facilities: Bar: Noon–11pm. Food: Meals available by prior request.

Comments: Fairly bland piece of land ... Average course for the area ... Good value ... Nice club course but not one for the visitor ... Rolling fairways, water hazards and clever bunkering make this a nice afternoon stroll.

Castlerock Golf Club ★★★★

Circular Road, Castlerock, County Londonderry BT51 4TJ
Nearest main town: Coleraine

Secretary: Mr R. McBride   Tel: 028 7084 8314
                                         Fax: 028 7084 9440
Professional: Mr R. Kelly

Playing: Midweek: round £25.00; day £40.00. Weekend: round
                  £35.00; day n/a. Handicap certificate required.

Facilities: Bar: 11am–11pm. Food: Breakfast, lunch and dinner
                  from 9am–9pm. Bar snacks.

Comments: So hard, even for the members ... Good par-3s ...
                  Pleasure to play ... Some unforgettable holes ... Does
                  the wind ever blow gently? ... Friendly bunch of
                  members ... White-knuckle stuff when the wind blows ...
                  Great course and good welcome.

City of Derry Golf Club ★★★

49 Victoria Road, Londonderry, County Londonderry BT47 2PQ
Nearest main town: Londonderry

Secretary: Mr H. Doherty   Tel: 028 7134 6369
                                         Fax: 028 7131 0008
Professional: Mr M. Doherty   Tel: 028 7134 6369
                                         Fax: 028 7131 0008

Playing: Midweek: round £20.00, with Member £10.00; day
                  n/a. Weekend: round £25.00, with Member £15.00;
                  day n/a. Handicap certificate required.

Facilities: Bar: Noon–11pm Mon/Fri, noon–midnight Sat,
                  noon–9pm Sunday. Food: Hours as for bar.

Comments: The championship Prehen course has picture-postcard
                  views over the River Foyle and the Donegal hills ... Lush
                  fairways thread their way through mature woodland ...
                  The legendary Walter Hagen played here and Fred Daly,
                  the only Irishman to win the Open, was professional for
                  six years.

Clandeboye Golf Club (Ava) ★★★

Conlig, Newtownards, County Down BT23 3PN
Nearest main town: Bangor

Secretary:	Mr W. Donald	Tel: 028 9127 1767
		Fax: 028 9147 3711
Professional:	Mr P. Gregory	Tel: 028 9127 1750

Playing: Midweek: round £20.00; day £35.00. Weekend: round £25.00; day n/a. Handicap certificate required.

Facilities: Bar: 11am–11pm. Food: Breakfast, lunch and dinner from 9am–9pm. Bar snacks.

Comments: Short and good fun ... par-5 second a beauty ... So much fun on this charming little course ... Views of Strangford Lough ... Keep your wits about you on this beguiling course.

Clandeboye Golf Club (Dufferin) ★★★

Conlig, Newtownards, County Down BT23 3PN
Nearest main town: Bangor

Secretary:	Mr W. Donald	Tel: 028 9127 1767
		Fax: 028 9147 3711
Professional:	Mr P. Gregory	Tel: 028 9127 1750

Playing: Midweek: round £25.00; day £35.00. Weekend: round £30.00; day n/a. Handicap certificate required.

Facilities: Bar: 11am–11pm. Food: Breakfast, lunch and dinner from 9am–9pm. Bar snacks.

Comments: Elevated greens, blind drives, streams, ditches – always something to watch out for ... Some long carries off the tee ... Woodland and heathland ... Drive on the 4th a terror ... High skill levels for this mature course.

County Cavan Golf Club ★★

Arnmore House, Drumelis, Cavan, County Cavan
Nearest main town: Cavan

| Secretary: | Mr J. Sheridan | Tel: 049 315041 |
| Professional: | Mr K. Carroll | Tel: 049 31388 |

Playing: Midweek: round £12.00; day £12.00. Weekend: round £14.00; day £14.00. Handicap certificate required.

Facilities: Bar: 10.30am–11pm. Food: Lunch and dinner from 10.30am–10pm. Bar snacks.

Comments: Parkland course ... Can get unplayable in winter ...
                  Local knowledge helps ... Very cheap green fee ... Fair
                  value for money for this unimaginative course.

Cruit Island Golf Club   ★★

Kincasslagh, Dunglow, County Donegal
Nearest main town: Donegal

Secretary: Mr D. Gallaway   Tel: 075 43296
Professional: None.

Playing: Midweek: round £10.00; day n/a. Weekend: round
                  £12.00; day n/a. Handicap certificate required.

Facilities: Bar: 11.30am–4pm. Food: Bar snacks.

Comments: Nine-hole course perched on the edge of the Atlantic
                  Ocean ... The 6th hole over the cove defies belief ...
                  With the Atlantic crashing against the rocks this is an
                  evocative experience ... Not in great condition but this
                  is golf back to its roots ... Don't let the fact it's half a
                  course put you off ... A blinder.

Donaghadee Golf Club   ★★

Warren Road, Donaghadee, County Down BT21 0PQ
Nearest main town: Belfast

Secretary: Mr K. Paton   Tel: 028 9188 3624
                                        Fax: 028 9188 8891
Professional: Mr G. Drew   Tel: 028 9188 2392

Playing: Midweek: round £14.00; day £20.00. Weekend: round
                  n/a; day n/a. Handicap certificate required.

Facilities: Bar: None. Food: None.

Comments: Open parkland course by the sea ... Intimidating final
                  hole with out of bounds left and right ... Stunning views
                  over the Copeland Islands to the Scottish coast, particu-
                  larly from the 16th tee ... Well appointed and friendly
                  clubhouse.

Donegal Golf Club ★★★★

Murvagh, Laghey, County Donegal
Nearest main town: Donegal

Secretary: Mr J. Nixon — Tel: 073 34054
Fax: 073 34377

Professional: None.

Playing: Midweek: round £20.00; day n/a. Weekend: round £27.00; day n/a. Handicap certificate required.

Facilities: Bar: 10.30am–11pm. Food: Lunch and dinner from 10am–9pm.

Comments: A sensational links ... Can't be bettered ... The match of any of Ireland's links legends ... Opened in 1960 but has an older feel to it ... Blue Stack Mountains dominate the course ... Longest course in Ireland ... Pray your driver is working ... Drive badly and you're out with the washing ... A Goliath of a course, felt like David ... Exciting ... Exhilarating.

Downpatrick Golf Club ★★

Saul Road, Downpatrick, County Down BT30 6PA
Nearest main town: Downpatrick

Secretary: Mr A. Vaughan — Tel: 028 4461 5947/2152
Professional: n/a — Tel: 028 4461 5167

Playing: Midweek: round £15.00; day £20.00. Weekend: round n/a; day n/a. Handicap certificate required.

Facilities: Bar: None. Food: None.

Comments: A challenging parkland course with some fiendishly tricky holes ... Downpatrick can boast the best scenery of any inland course in Ulster with panoramic views over Strangford Lough and the Mountains of Mourne ... Even the Isle of Man comes into view on a clear day.

Dungannon Golf Club ★★★

34 Springfield Lane, Mullaghmore, Dungannon, County Tyrone
Nearest main town: Dungannon

Secretary: Mr L. Agnew — Tel: 028 8772 2098
Fax: 028 8772 7338

Professional: None.

Playing: Midweek: round n/a; day £20.00. Weekend: round n/a; day £25.00. Handicap certificate required.

Facilities: Bar: 11am–11pm. Food: Lunch and dinner from noon–7pm. Bar snacks.

Comments: Hilly in places but good way to work off hospitality … Always enjoy society days here … Established course with a nice feel … Standard scratch is three under par … A proper club with progressive attitude.

Dunmurry Golf Club   ★★

91 Dunmurry Lane, Dunmurry, County Belfast BT17 9JS
Nearest main town: Belfast

Secretary: Mr I. McBride   Tel: 028 9061 0834
                                      Fax: 028 9060 2540
Professional: Mr J. Dolan   Tel: 028 9062 1314

Playing: Midweek: round £17.00; day n/a. Weekend: round £26.50; day n/a. Handicap certificate required.

Facilities: Bar: 10.30am–11pm. Food: Lunch and dinner from 9am–9pm, except Mon.

Comments: Nice club with a relaxed atmosphere … Popular venue but course is suffering … Opened in 1983 but has matured well … Fair value at this open-to-all, friendly club.

Edenmore Golf Club

Drumnabreeze Road, Magheralin, Craigavon, County Armagh BT67 0RH
Nearest main town: Lurgan

Secretary: Mr K. Logan   Tel: 028 9261 1310
                                      Fax: 028 9261 3310
Professional: None.

Playing: Midweek: round £12.00–£13.00; day £14.00. Weekend: round n/a; day n/a. Handicap certificate required.

Facilities: Bar: None. Food: None.

Comments: Laid out in the gently rolling hills of the Lower Lagan Valley ... A relatively open front nine transcends into a mature inward half where many aged trees have been integrated into severed holes ... A pleasurable golfing experience awaits at Edenmore.

Fortwilliam Golf Club ★★

Downview Avenue, Belfast, County Down B15 4EZ
Nearest main town: Belfast

Secretary:	Mr M. Purdy	Tel: 028 9037 0770
		Fax: 028 9078 1891
Professional:	Mr P. Hanna	Tel: 028 9077 0980

Playing: Midweek: round £20.00; day £27.00. Weekend: round n/a; day n/a. Handicap certificate required.

Facilities: Bar: None. Food: None.

Comments: A parkland course dominated by the heavily wooded 'Cavehill' which rises to over 1000 feet above sea level and makes an attractive backdrop to many holes ... Well stocked professional shop.

Foyle International Golf Centre ★★

12 Alder Road, Londonderry, County Londonderry BT48 8DB
Nearest main town: Londonderry

Secretary:	Ms M. Lapsley	Tel: 028 7135 2222
		Fax: 028 7135 3967
Professional:	Mr K. McLaughlin	Tel: 028 7135 2222
		Fax: 028 7135 3967

Playing: Midweek: round £11.00; day n/a. Weekend: round £14.00; day n/a. Handicap certificate required.

Facilities: Bar: Noon–1am. Food: Available seven days a week.

Comments: An exciting but fair challenge for beginners and veterans alike ... In addition to the championship course, Foyle boasts a 9-hole par-3 course, a 19-bay driving range and the highly acclaimed Pitcher's Restaurant.

Holywood Golf Club ★★

Nuns Walk, Demesne Road, Holywood, County Down BT18 9LE
Nearest main town: Belfast

Secretary: Mr S. Melville   Tel: 028 9042 3135
(Gen. Manager)   Club: 028 9042 2138
Fax: 028 9042 5040
Professional: Mr M. Bannon   Tel: 028 9042 5503

Playing: Midweek: round £15.00; day £21.00. Weekend: round n/a. Visitors exc. 1.30pm–2.15pm; Saturday after 5pm. Handicap certificate required.

Facilities: Bar: None. Food:

Comments: Enjoyable parkland layout ... Majority of the holes are tree-lined but the fairways are not too tight, even for the higher handicapper ... Friendly welcome ... Well established course in good condition ... Excellent value for money.

Kilkeel Golf Club ★★

Mourne Park, Kilkeel, County Down BT34 4LB
Nearest main town: Kilkeel

Secretary: Mr S. McBride   Tel: 028 4176 2296
Fax: 028 4176 5095
Professional: None.

Playing: Midweek: round n/a; day £16.00. Weekend: round n/a; day £20.00. Handicap certificate required.

Facilities: Bar: 11am–11pm. Food: Lunch and dinner from noon–8pm. Bar snacks.

Comments: An excellent test on a scenic course ... Kept in reasonable condition ... Beautiful views in every direction ... Parkland course at the foot of the Mourne Mountains ... Quite an English feel to this parkland course ... Inland gem with great potential ... Mature woodland lends this course a regal air.

Kirkistown Castle Golf Club

142 Main Road, Newtownards, County Down BT22 1JA
Nearest main town: Belfast

Secretary: Mr G. Graham   Tel: 028 4277 1233
                                         Fax: 028 4277 1699
Professional: Mr J. Peden   Tel: 028 4277 1004

Playing: Midweek: round £13.00; day £13.00. Weekend: round £20.00; day £20.00. Handicap certificate required.

Facilities: Bar: 11am–11pm. Food: Breakfast, lunch and dinner from 9am–9pm. Bar snacks.

Comments: A hidden gem that is worth taking the trouble to find ... Never gets wet underfoot ... Parkland/links with strategic bunkering ... Stunning location and excellent condition ... Drainage super ... Consistent, quality course.

Letterkenny Golf Club   ★

Barnhill, Letterkenny, County Donegal
Nearest main town: Letterkenny

Secretary: Mr I. Mackenzie   Tel: 074 21150
Professional: None.

Playing: Midweek: round £12.00; day n/a. Weekend: round £15.00; day n/a. Handicap certificate required.

Facilities: Bar: 10.30am–11pm. Food: Bar snacks.

Comments: Lovely new clubhouse but course prone to damp ground ... Well presented and enjoyable ... Beautiful 11th hole ... Two halves to this course, the plateau holes get the nod ... Not much variety ... Not in the top rank for Donegal ... Did not do much for my game.

Lisburn Golf Club

68 Eglantine Road, Lisburn, County Antrim BT27 5RQ
Nearest main town: Lisburn

Secretary: Mr G. McVeigh   Tel: 028 9267 7216
                                         Fax: 028 9260 3608
Professional: Mr B. Campbell   Tel: 028 9267 7217

Playing: Midweek: round £25.00; day n/a. Weekend: round £25.00; day n/a. Handicap certificate required.

Facilities: Bar: 11am–11pm. Food: Lunch and dinner from 11am–9pm. Bar snacks.

Comments: Well laid out with lots of bunkers ... Good pro shop ... Well maintained with picturesque holes ... Very tranquil ... Finishes with a wonderful par-3.

Lurgan Golf Club ★★

The Demesne, Lurgan, County Armagh BT67 9BN
Nearest main town: Lurgan

Secretary: Mrs G. Turkington   Tel: 028 3832 2087
                                      Fax: 028 3832 5306
Professional: Mr D. Paul   Tel: 028 3832 1068

Playing: Midweek: round £15.00; day n/a. Weekend: round £20.00; day n/a. Handicap certificate required.

Facilities: Bar: 11am–11pm. Food: Lunch and dinner by arrangement.

Comments: Internal out-of-bounds is annoying ... Set by Lurgan Lake ... Opportunity to open your shoulders on this flat expanse of a golf course ... Not high quality but cheap and cheerful.

Mahee Island Golf Club

Comber, Belfast, County Down BT23 6ET
Nearest main town: Belfast

Secretary: Mr A. McCracken   Tel: 028 9754 1234
                 (Steward)
Professional: None.

Playing: Midweek: round £10.00; day n/a. Weekend: round £15.00; day n/a. Handicap certificate required.

Facilities: Bar: None. Food: Lunch and dinner from noon–3pm. Bar snacks.

Comments: Top-of-the-drawer 9-hole course on island in Strangford Lough ... Idyllic location on an island ... Best maintained 9-hole course in Ireland ... Bizarre but beautiful ... Predominantly in good condition ... One primarily for the enthusiast ... Poor off-course facilities.

Malone Golf Club   ★★★

240 Upper Malone Road, Dunmurry, County Belfast BT17 9LB
Nearest main town: Belfast

Secretary:	Mr J. Agate	Tel: 028 9061 2758
		Fax: 028 9043 1394
Professional:	Mr M. McGee	Tel: 028 9061 4917
		Fax: 028 9061 4917

Playing: Midweek: round £33.00; day £33.00. Weekend: round £38.00; day £38.00. Handicap certificate required.

Facilities: Bar: 11am–11pm. Food: Breakfast, lunch and dinner from 9am–9pm. Bar snacks.

Comments: One of the best parkland courses in the area ... In top condition, hardly a divot to be seen ... Rolling hills, water, sand – it has it all ... Magnificent clubhouse ... Very British course ... Opened in the 60s and still in fine nick.

Massereene Golf Club   ★★★

51 Lough Road, Antrim, County Antrim BT41 4DQ
Nearest main town: Antrim

Secretary:	Mrs S. Greene	Tel: 028 9442 8096
		Fax: 028 9448 7661
Professional:	Mr J. Smyth	Tel: 028 9446 4074

Playing: Midweek: round £20.00; day n/a. Weekend: round £25.00; day n/a. Handicap certificate required.

Facilities: Bar: 11am–11pm. Food: Lunch from 11am–9pm.

Comments: A well-manicured, attractive course, very pleasing to the eye ... Very underrated but they like it that way ... Course has been fiddled with over the years ... Sporting and stylish ... Will make a point of returning to this parkland course.

Nairn & Portnoo Golf Club   ★★★

Nairn, Portnoo, County Donegal
Nearest main town: Ardara

Secretary:	Mr E. Bonner	Tel: 075 45107
		Fax: 074 25185

Professional: None.

Playing: Midweek: round £13.00; day £13.00. Weekend: round £16.00; day £16.00. Handicap certificate required.

Facilities: Bar: 10.30am–11pm. Food: Bar snacks.

Comments: Terrific potential – remove the cattle and caravans at the start and finish, upgrade the clubhouse, a few new tees and you would have a great course ... Windswept links ... Great hospitality and places to stay ... Starts poorly but gets better ... Popular course ... Respected venue almost deserted outside summer.

North West Golf Club   ★

Lisfannon, Fahan, County Donegal
Nearest main town: Buncrana

Secretary: Mr D. Coyle   Tel: 077 61027
                                   Fax: 077 63284
Professional: Mr S. McBriarty   Tel: 077 61715

Playing: Midweek: round £15.00; day £15.00. Weekend: round £20.00; day £20.00. Handicap certificate required.

Facilities: Bar: 10.30am–11pm. Food: Lunch and dinner from noon–9pm.

Comments: A second-string course in Donegal but has attractions in itself ... Flattish links near the Mouldy mountains ... Good atmosphere at this out-of-the-way club.

Nuremore Hotel & Golf Club

Carrickmacross, Nuremore, County Monaghan
Nearest main town: Carrickmacross

Secretary: Mr M. Cassidy   Tel: 042 61438
                                     Fax: 042 61853
Professional: Mr M. Cassidy   Tel: 042 64016

Playing: Midweek: round £20.00; day £20.00. Weekend: round £25.00; day £25.00. Handicap certificate required.

Facilities: Bar: 10.30am–11pm. Food: Breakfast, lunch and dinner from 9am–9pm. Bar snacks.

Comments: Scary tee shot on the 10th ... Hotel dominates this attractive parkland course ... Some short par-4s that make you think ... Picturesque drumlins and lakes ... Impressive finishing hole.

Portadown Golf Club ★

192 Gilford Road, Portadown, County Armagh BT63 5LF
Nearest main town: Portadown

Secretary: Mrs M. Holloway   Tel: 028 3835 5356
                                      Fax: 028 3835 5356
Professional: Mr P. Stevenson   Tel: 028 3833 4655
                                      Fax: 028 3836 1947

Playing: Midweek: round £17.00; day n/a. Weekend: round £22.00; day n/a. Handicap certificate required.

Facilities: Bar: 11am–11pm. Food: Lunch and dinner from 11am–9pm, except Mondays.

Comments: Flattish, fun course in parkland setting ... River Bann provides a nice natural framing for a few holes ... 9th over the river is impressive ... Variety of doglegs and straightaway holes.

Portsalon Golf Club ★★★★

Portsalon, County Donegal
Nearest main town: Letterkenny

Secretary: Mr P. Doherty   Tel: 074 59459
                                      Fax: 074 59459
Professional: None.

Playing: Midweek: round £14.00; day £14.00. Weekend: round £17.00; day £17.00. Handicap certificate required.

Facilities: Bar: 10.30am–11pm. Food: Lunch and dinner from noon–9pm.

Comments: Try playing to your handicap here ... A course to play for the rest of your life ... Great names – the Ballymostocker Bay and Knockalla mountains ... Basic club ... Learn all about the unpredictability of links golf here ... In the summer the ball kicks everywhere ... Charming people ... Made welcome ... So unique ... Can't wait to return.

Portstewart Golf Club (Strand)   ★★★★

117 Strand Road, Portstewart, County Londonderry BT55 7PG
Nearest main town: Portstewart

Secretary:	Mr M. Moss	Tel: 028 7083 3839
		Fax: 028 7083 4097
Professional:	Mr A. Hunter	Tel: 028 7083 2601

Playing: Midweek: round £45.00; day £65.00. Weekend: round £65.00; day n/a. Handicap certificate required.

Facilities: Bar: 11am–11pm. Food: Breakfast, lunch and dinner from 9am–9pm. Bar snacks.

Comments: Exhilarating experience ... The pro seems to remember every visitor ... Staff and members top drawer ... Wonderful first nine holes designed by the club's members ... Very friendly pro ... Cosy, friendly clubhouse ... I could play this course every day ... Could not believe the tee-shot at the 2nd ... Redesigned in 1990 with seven new holes.

Radisson Roe Park Golf Club   ★★★

Limavaddy, County Londonderry BT49 9LB
Nearest main town: Limavaddy

Secretary:	Mr D. Brockerton	Tel: 028 7772 2212
		Fax: 028 7772 2313
Professional:	Mr S. Duffy	

Playing: Midweek: round £20.00; day £20.00. Weekend: round £20.00; day £20.00. Handicap certificate required.

Facilities: Bar: 11am–11pm. Food: Breakfast, lunch and dinner from 9am–9pm. Bar snacks.

Comments: Very testing parkland course with excellent facilities at good prices ... Interesting layout with pleasant clubhouse ... Lough Foyle and the Inishowen peninsula form the backdrop ... Beautifully sculptured course with US-style features.

Rockmount Golf Club   ★★

28 Drumalig Road, Belfast, County Down BT8 8EQ
Nearest main town: Belfast

Secretary: Mr R. Patterson   Tel: 028 9081 2279
                  (Proprietor)   Fax: 028 9081 5851
Professional: None.

Playing: Midweek: round: up to 10 players £20, 11–20 £19,
                  21–40 £18, over 40 £17; day n/a. Weekend: round: up
                  to 10 players £24, 11–20 £23, 21–40 £22, over 40
                  £21; day n/a. Handicap certificate required.

Facilities: Bar: 11am–11pm. Food: All day.

Comments: A little masterpiece set in the quiet of the County Down
                  countryside with scenic views of the Mourne Mountains
                  ... The signature hole has a touch of Pete Dye about it
                  with a demanding approach shot into a green fronted
                  with water ... Excellent clubhouse restaurant.

Rosapenna Hotel Golf Club   ★★★★

Redcastle, Moville, County Donegal
Nearest main town: Londonderry

Secretary: Mr F. Cassey   Tel: 074 55301
                                           Fax: 074 55128
Professional: Mr D. Patterson

Playing: Midweek: round £20.00; day n/a. Weekend: round
                  £25.00; day n/a. Handicap certificate required.

Facilities: Bar: 10.30am–11pm. Food: Breakfast, lunch and
                  dinner from 7am–10pm. Bar snacks.

Comments: A peaceful place to play with 18 holes of good standard
                  ... Laid out by Old Tom Morris ... This, Portsalon and
                  Ballyliffin should meet all your golfing needs in Donegal
                  ... Unknown links of substantial character ... Fairly
                  facile links without ruggedness of other Irish courses ...
                  If you play here only on holidays, you will never match
                  your handicap.

The Royal Belfast Golf Club   ★★

Holywood, Craigavad, County Belfast BT19 0BP
Nearest main town: Belfast

Secretary: Mrs S. Morrison   Tel: 028 9042 8165
                                           Fax: 028 9042 1404

Professional: Mr S. Spence   Tel: 028 9042 8586

Playing: Midweek: round £30.00; day n/a. Weekend: round £40.00; day n/a. Handicap certificate required.

Facilities: Bar: 11am–11pm. Food: Lunch from noon–3pm. Dinner by arrangement.

Comments: Very exclusive club ... If you can get on, fairly cheap for an exclusive club ... Oldest established club in Ireland ... Course condition always good ... Not as windy as other links ... Protected by over 60 bunkers ... Simple off the tee, problems start around the greens.

Royal Portrush Golf Club (Valley)   ★★★★

Dunluce Road, Portrush, County Antrim BT56 8JQ
Nearest main town: Portrush

Secretary: Miss W. Erskine   Tel: 028 7082 2311
                                        Fax: 028 7082 3139
Professional: Mr D. Stevenson   Tel: 028 7082 3335

Playing: Midweek: round £24.00; day £34.00. Weekend: round £32.00; day £42.00. Handicap certificate required.

Facilities: Bar: 11am–11pm. Food: Lunch (included in round fee) from 11am–3pm. Dinner by arrangement.

Comments: A deserved respite after the Dunluce ... Bites hard when you least expect it ... Wee sister to the Dunluce but top of my list every time ... 'Feel' course ... Didn't even consider playing it after the Dunluce ... A bit 'after the Lord Mayor's show'.

Scrabo Golf Club

233 Scrabo Road, Newtownards, County Down BT23 4SL
Nearest main town: Newtownards

Secretary: Ms C. Hamill   Tel: 028 9181 2355
              (General Manager)   Fax: 028 9182 2919
Professional: Mr P. McCrystal   Tel: 028 9181 7848
                                        Fax: 028 9182 2919

Playing: Midweek: round £15.00; day n/a. Weekend: round £20.00; day visitors not permitted Saturday before 4pm. Handicap certificate required.

Facilities: Bar: Monday–Saturday, 11.30am–11pm. Sunday 12.30pm–10pm. Food: Available every day except Monday.

Comments: Well established and mature course ... Scenic views from the upland holes ... Made very welcome ... Excellent catering ... Good value for money and enjoyable round in a scenic setting ... Not really all that challenging.

Slieve Russell Golf Club ★★★

Ballconnell, County Cavan
Nearest main town: Cavan

Secretary: Mr P. Creamer   Tel: 049 26458
                                      Fax: 049 26474
Professional: Mr L. McCool   Tel: 049 26444
                                      Fax: 049 26640

Playing: Midweek: round £30.00; day n/a. Weekend: round £38.00; day n/a. Handicap certificate required.

Facilities: Bar: 10.30am–11pm. Food: Lunch and dinner from 10.30am–9pm. Bar snacks.

Comments: Excellent new course ... Facilities and course first class ... Very linksy feel to this parkland beauty with huge contoured greens and deep greenside bunkers ... Exciting par-3s and birdieable par-5s ... Had a memorable weekend at the hotel and course – will return one day.

The Spa Golf Club ★★

20 Grove Road, Ballynahinch, County Down BT24 8PN
Nearest main town: Ballynahinch

Secretary: Mr T. Magee   Tel: 028 9756 2365
                                     Fax: 028 9756 4158
Professional: Club Shop – no Professional

Playing: Midweek: round £15.00; day n/a. Weekend: round £20.00; day n/a. Handicap certificate required.

Facilities: Bar: 11am–11pm. Food: Every day 10am–9pm.

Comments: Nothing special in playing terms, but offers some scenic views of the mountains ... Testing enough to keep most average golfers on their toes for all 18-holes ... Pleasant parkland setting in reasonably generous fairways and medium paced greens ... Good value but don't expect a championship quality layout.

Templepatrick Golf Club ★★★★

Stakis Park Hotel, Templepatrick, County Antrim BT39 0DD
Nearest main town: Templepatrick (5 mins Belfast Int'l Airport)

Secretary: Mr W. Donald Tel: 028 9443 5500
(Director of Golf) Fax: 028 9443 5511
Professional: None.

Playing: Midweek: round £30.00; day Residents £20.00. Weekend: round £35.00; day Residents £25.00. Handicap certificate required.

Facilities: Bar: Full facilities at Stakis Park Hotel. Food: Full facilities at Stakis Park Hotel.

Comments: Designed by David Jones, one of Northern Ireland's finest golfers ... Tall slim trees dominate the course ... The course was originally very wet, so natural lakes provide natural hazards but 30 more bunkers and 100,000 more trees are planned ... With its attractive rope-rail bridges and wildlife, it is a welcome addition to Ireland's golfing heritage.

The Belvoir Park Golf Club ★★★★

Church Road, Newtownbreda, Belfast, County Belfast BT8 4AN
Nearest main town: Belfast

Secretary: Mr K. Graham Tel: 028 9049 1693
Fax: 028 9064 6113
Professional: Mr G. Kelly Tel: 028 9064 6714

Playing: Midweek: round £33.00; day £33.00. Weekend: round £38.00; day £38.00. Handicap certificate required.

Facilities: Bar: 11am–11pm. Food: Lunch and dinner from 11am–9pm. Bar snacks.

Comments: Best inland course in Northern Ireland ... Lush fairways on this rejuvenated course ... Hilly in places ... Highly rated ... Close to Belfast but an apparent oasis of calm ... Nice pro shop and accommodating to visitors.

The Knock Club ★★★

Summerfield, Dundonald, County Belfast BT16 0QX
Nearest main town: Belfast

Secretary: Mr S. Managh   Tel: 028 9048 3251
                                     Fax: 028 9048 3251
Professional: Mr G. Fairweather   Tel: 028 9048 3825

Playing: Midweek: round £20.00; day n/a. Weekend: round £25.00; day n/a. Handicap certificate required.

Facilities: Bar: 11am–11pm. Food: Lunch and dinner from 11am–9pm. Bar snacks.

Comments: A tree-lined course that can get wet in winter ... Have a hearty breakfast before you go out ... Needs good drives ... Busy at weekends ... Most fairways tree-lined ... Watch your driving ... All the problems laid out clearly before you.

Warrenpoint Golf Club ★★

Lower Dromore Road, Warrenpoint, County Down BT34 3LN
Nearest main town: Newry

Secretary: Mrs M. Trainor   Tel: 028 4175 2219
              (Manager)   Fax: 028 4175 2918
Professional: Mr N. Shaw   Tel: 028 4175 2371
                                     Fax: 028 4175 2371

Playing: Midweek: round £20.00; day n/a. Weekend: round £27.00; day n/a. Handicap certificate required.

Facilities: Bar: 11am–11pm. Food: Lunch and dinner from noon–9pm. Bar snacks.

Comments: Simply breathtaking scenery ... Very hilly parkland course ... Not very hard but you come here for the views not the golf ... If you're in the area you're probably coming to County Down, not here.

Connacht

County Sligo Golf Club ★★★★★

Rosses Point, County Dublin
Nearest main town: Sligo

The rich seams of golf that exist in south-west Ireland gradually disappear as you pass through Galway and up through County Roscommon. Eventually you reach the town of Sligo, from where it is a short drive to Rosses Point, a golf course that is undoubtedly the best in this part of the Republic. Dominated by the majestic mountain of Ben Bulben, from which the small villages, beaches and crofters' cottages take their character, Rosses Point is a treat to play.

It is a traditional links course, the standard perils of bunkers, heavy rough and wind dictating the course and pace of play. But its character is not built on that alone. The subtleties of the slightly undulating fairways and positions and angles of the green make it a real 'feel' course, harmonising your game with the rhythm of the land.

The poetry of William Yeats used to speak fondly of this part of the world (he is buried in nearby Drumcliff), and visitors do fall under its charm, many leaving with the impression of Rosses Point as the finest links in Ireland. Certainly, it is incredibly fair, far removed from the traditional image of a links with its harsh bounces and cruel kicks.

One of the course's most memorable holes is the 5th, with its astonishing view of Ben Bulben. A par-5 named 'The Jump', you drive from an elevated tee to a fairway that hugs the cliff line from where, if you're lucky, you could be faced with a long iron or, more realistically, a lay-up in front of the tiny green. The feeling of the hole shrinking, and getting more difficult as you walk each yard from the tee, is technically very strong. That could also be said of the 17th, a par-4 played down into a gully, before climbing spectacularly to a hidden green protected on all sides. The incline and green all slope back towards you and one can imagine professional players spinning the ball back down the slope.

You may prefer the gung-ho thrillers of Waterville or Tralee with their enormous dunes, but you can't fail to be impressed with Rosses Point.

Secretary: Mr R. Dunne   Tel: 071 77134
                                      Fax: 071 77460
Professional: Mr L. Robinson   Tel: 071 77171

Playing: Midweek: round £32.00; day £48.00. Weekend: round £40.00; day £60.00. Handicap certificate required.

Facilities: Bar: 10.30am–11pm. Food: Lunch and dinner from 10am–9pm. Bar snacks.

Comments: Great stretch of golf in the middle of the round ... Ben Bulben lends this links a mystical feel ... So natural, so magical ... Played it every year on holiday for the last 20 years ... Good putting green and clubhouse ... Very natural, the wind is its defence ... Basic facilities ... Views of the Atlantic and the Bay of Drumcliff ... Exceptional.

Athenry Golf Club ★★

Palmerstown, Oranmore, County Galway
Nearest main town: Galway

Secretary: Mr P. Flattery   Tel: 091 794466
                                     Fax: 091 794971
Professional: Mr R. Ryan

Playing: Midweek: round £15.00; day n/a. Weekend: round £18.00; day n/a. Handicap certificate required.

Facilities: Bar: 10am–11.30pm. Food: Restaurant and bar food.

Comments: Easy to find, only half a mile from the main Galway–Dublin road ... Excellent condition, drains very well for an inland course ... Greens were outstanding ... First class clubhouse facilities ... Real pleasure to play.

Athlone Golf Club

Hodson Bay, Athlone, County Roscommon
Nearest main town: Athlone

Secretary: Mr T. Corry   Tel: 0902 92073
                                  Fax: 0902 94080
Professional: Mr M. Quinn

Playing: Midweek: round £18.00; day n/a. Weekend: round £20.00; day n/a. Handicap certificate required.

Facilities: Bar: 10.30am–11pm. Food: Breakfast, lunch and dinner from 9am–9pm. Bar snacks.

Comments: Warmth and hospitality through and through ...
Overlooking Lough Ree ... Fun course with short par-5s
... Straightforward course where you can feel good
about your game ... Bunkers provide major headache.

Ballinasloe Golf Club   ★★

Portuhna Road, Ballinasloe, County Galway
Nearest main town: Ballinasloe

Secretary: Mr M. Kelly   Tel: 0905 42126
                                           Fax: 0905 42538
Professional: None.

Playing: Midweek: round £12.00 (£10.00 before 10.00am
                    Mon–Fri); day n/a. Weekend: round £12.00; day n/a.
                    Handicap certificate required.

Facilities: Bar: Weekend 9am–11pm. Weekdays 3pm–11pm.
                    Food: Weekend 9am–11pm. Weekday 3pm–11pm.

Comments: Extended to 18 holes in 1984, this well-maintained
                    course is not too difficult and hence is very popular with
                    holiday golfers ... Excellent fairways and greens.

Connemara Golf Club   ★★★★

Ballyconnelly, County Galway
Nearest main town: Clifden

Secretary: Mr J. McLaughlin   Tel: 095 23502
                                           Fax: 095 23662
Professional: Mr H. O'Neill   Tel: 095 23502

Playing: Midweek: round £30.00; day £45.00. Weekend: round
                    £30.00; day £45.00. Handicap certificate required.

Facilities: Bar: 10.30am–11pm. Food: Lunch and dinner from
                    10am–9pm.

Comments: Great location and excellent food ... Course in need of
                    more rough ... Spectacular setting and true Irish weather
                    ... Stunning setting ... Should be on every golfer's 'must
                    play' list ... Romantic course that gets going on the back
                    nine ... Rough and fairway bunkers will catch you soon
                    enough ... Would be the best in Ireland if you judged it
                    on the back nine.

Craddockstown Golf Course ★★

Blessington Road, Naas, County Kildare
Nearest main town: Naas

Secretary:	Mr L. Watson	Tel: 045 897610
		Fax: 045 896968

Professional: None.

Playing: Midweek: round £14.00; day £18.00. Weekend: round n/a; day n/a. Handicap certificate required.

Facilities: Bar: None. Food: None.

Comments: A maturing parkland course with some excellent short holes ... Well-protected greens and tricky fairway water hazards ensure a fair test of golf.

Enniscrone Golf Club ★★★★

Ballina Road, Enniscrone, County Sligo
Nearest main town: Enniscrone

Secretary:	To be appointed.	Tel: 096 36297
		Fax: 096 36657
Professional:	Mr C. McGoldrick	Tel: 096 36666

Playing: Midweek: round £25.00; day n/a. Weekend: round £34.00; day n/a. Handicap certificate required.

Facilities: Bar: 10.30am–11pm. Food: Lunch and dinner from 10am–9pm. Bar snacks.

Comments: Beautiful location with great variety of holes ... A natural links, play it two or three times to know it ... A gem for very little money to play and eat ... Best holes are on the back nine among the dunes ... Contrasting nines, but both have their own appeal.

Galway Golf Club ★★★★

Blackrock, Galway, County Galway
Nearest main town: Galway

Secretary:	Mr P. Fahy	Tel: 091 522169
		Fax: 091 529783
Professional:	Mr D. Wallace	Tel: 091 523038

Playing: Midweek: round £18.00; day n/a. Weekend: round £23.00; day n/a. Handicap certificate required.

Facilities: Bar: 10.30am–11pm. Food: Lunch and dinner from 10am–9pm.

Comments: Views over Galway Bay ... Outdated course in need of spicing up ... Greens variable on visit ... Old course with an indefinable spirit and mystery ... Very tight and difficult ... Came away having ballooned over my handicap.

Galway Bay Golf & Country Club ★★★

Renville, Oranmore, County Galway
Nearest main town: Galway

Secretary: Mr J. Cassidy   Tel: 091 790500
                                    Fax: 091 792510
Professional: Mr E. O'Connor   Tel: 091 790503

Playing: Midweek: round £35.00; day £50.00. Weekend: round £40.00; day £60.00. Handicap certificate required.

Facilities: Bar: 10.30am–11pm. Food: Breakfast, lunch and dinner from 7am–10pm. Bar snacks.

Comments: If there was no wind it would be a doddle ... Wind can get horrific ... Play this with a hangover and you'll soon blow the cobwebs away ... Exhilarating experience which I'll never forget ... Overlooking the Atlantic and Galway Bay ... Ordinary land turned into something special by Christy O'Connor Jr.

Gort Golf Club

Castlequater, Gort, County Galway
Nearest main town: Galway

Secretary: Mr S. Devlin   Tel: 091 632244
Professional: None.

Playing: Midweek: round £12.00; day £12.00. Weekend: round £12.00; day £12.00. Handicap certificate required.

Facilities: Bar: 10.30am–11pm. Food: Bar snacks.

Comments: An old club built on a new site ... Excellent greens and tight fairways ... Opened recently and excellent addition to region's quota of courses.

Gweedore Golf Club ★★

Magheragallon, Derrybeg, Letterkenny, County Donegal
Nearest main town: Letterkenny

Secretary: Mr O. Ferry   Tel: 075 31543
Professional: None.

Playing: Midweek: round £8.00; day n/a. Weekend: round
                 £10.00; day n/a. Handicap certificate required.

Facilities: Bar: 10am–midnight. Food: Full catering during
                 summer.

Comments: An attractive 9-hole seaside course providing an enjoy-
                 able test for the holiday golfer ... Great value golf in a
                 terrific part of Ireland.

Loughrea Golf Club ★

Graigue, Loughrea, County Galway
Nearest main town: Galway

Secretary: Mrs M. Hawkin   Tel: 091 841049
Professional: None.

Playing: Midweek: round £12.00; day n/a. Weekend: round
                 £12.00; day n/a. Handicap certificate required.

Facilities: Bar: 10.30am–11pm. Food: Breakfast, lunch and
                 dinner from 9am–9pm. Bar snacks.

Comments: Very short and cheap course ... Great value for money
                 ... Nothing special about the course ... Parkland course
                 extended to 18 holes in early 1990s.

Newlands Golf Course

Clondalkin, Dublin 22, County Dublin
Nearest main town: Dublin

Secretary: Mr A. O'Neill   Tel: 01 459 3157/2903
                                          Fax: 01 459 3498
Professional: Mr K. O'Donnell   Tel: 01 459 3538

Playing: Midweek: round IR£32.00; day n/a. Weekend: round
                 n/a; day n/a. Handicap certificate required.

Facilities: Bar: None. Food: None.

Comments: A testing parkland course where many of the holes demand precisely struck approach shots ... The tough finishing hole is an uphill par-5 with out-of-bounds on the left and trees bordering on the right.

Oughterard Golf Club   ★★

Oughterard, County Galway
Nearest main town: Oughterard 1.5 miles

Secretary: Mr J. Waters   Tel: 091 552131
                                          Fax: 091 552733
Professional: Mr M. Ryan   Tel: 091 552131
                                          Fax: 091 552733

Playing: Midweek: round £20.00; day n/a. Weekend: round £22.00; day n/a. Handicap certificate required.

Facilities: Bar: 11am–midnight. Food: All day – full facilities.

Comments: Situated on the shores of Lough Corrib, on the road to Connemara ... Recently updated under the expert guidance of Patrick Merrigan ... Well worth a visit ... Fine clubhouse.

Portarlington Golf Club   ★★

Garryhinch, Portarlington, County Laois
Nearest main town: Portarlington

Secretary: Mr M. Turley   Tel: 0502 23351
Professional: None.

Playing: Midweek: round £14.00; day n/a. Weekend: round £17.00; day n/a. Handicap certificate required.

Facilities: Bar: From 11am. Food: Available all day.

Comments: Layout is dominated by large stands of mature trees ... Water comes into play on several holes and the river flowing through the course makes the closing holes especially challenging ... Very scenic setting ... Friendly welcome.

Roscommon Golf Club   ★

Moate Park, Roscommon, County Roscommon
Nearest main town: Roscommon

Secretary: Mr B. Campbell Tel: 0903 26382
                                Fax: 0903 26043
Professional: None.

Playing: Midweek: round £15.00; day £15.00. Weekend: round £15.00; day £15.00. Handicap certificate required.

Facilities: Bar: 10.30am–11pm. Food: Lunch and dinner from noon–6pm.

Comments: Recently extended to 18 holes ... You're not missing anything if you drive past ... The extra nine does not hide the course's weaknesses ... Cheap and cheerful.

Seapoint Golf Club ★★

Termonkeckin, Drogheda, County Louth
Nearest main town: Drogheda

Secretary: Mr K. Carrie   Tel: 041 982 2333
                               Fax: 041 982 2331
Professional: Mr D. Carroll Tel: 041 988 1066
                                 Fax: 041 982 2331

Playing: Midweek: round £30.00 winter/£25.00 summer; day n/a. Weekend: round £36.00 winter/£30.00 summer; day n/a. Handicap certificate required.

Facilities: Bar: 11am–7pm winter/11am–11pm summer. Food: Restaurant, snacks and à la carte.

Comments: Fairly new course, first opened ten years ago ... Designed by Irish European Tour player, Des Smyth ... Fine links-style layout ... Some of the carries off the tees can be a bit daunting for the shorter hitters. Short holes often don't play all that short ... Wind big factor.

Stackstown Golf Course ★★

Kellystown Road, Rathfarnham, Dublin 16, County Dublin
Nearest main town: Dublin

Secretary: Mr K. Lawlor   Tel: 01 494 1993
Professional: Mr M. Kavanagh Tel: 01 944561

Playing: Midweek: round £16.00; day £20.00. Weekend: round n/a; day n/a. Handicap certificate required.

Facilities: Bar: None. Food: None.

Comments: Set in the foothills of the Dublin mountains with splendid views of Dublin City and Bay ... Padraig Harrington, of Ryder Cup fame, started his golfing career here at the age of ten.

Strandhill Golf Club   ★

Strandhill, County Sligo
Nearest main town: Sligo

Secretary: Mrs S. Corcoran   Tel: 071 68188
                                            Fax: 071 68811
Professional: None.   Tel: 071 68725

Playing: Midweek: round £15.00; day n/a. Weekend: round £20.00; day n/a. Handicap certificate required.

Facilities: Bar: 10.30am–11pm. Food: Lunch and dinner from noon–9pm. Bar snacks.

Comments: Under-rated, can be very tough with some unusual par-3s ... Unknown links with views of mountains ... Some memorable, friendly times here ... Too short to test the advanced player.

Tuam Golf Club

Barnacurragh, Tuam, County Galway
Nearest main town: Tuam

Secretary: Mr V. Gaffney   Tel: 093 28993
                                            Fax: 093 26003
Professional: Mr L. Smyth   Tel: 093 24091
                                            Fax: 086 814 3050

Playing: Midweek: round £15.00; day n/a. Weekend: round £15.00; day n/a. Handicap certificate required.

Facilities: Bar: Normal opening hours. Food: Tea, snacks. Lunch meals can be provided.

Comments: 18-hole par-72 parkland course 6000 metres in length ... Lots of wildlife – you may have to ask the foxes if you can play through ... Ladies watch out for the lake in front of the 4th green ... Friendly welcome always guaranteed ... Grand in the summer.

Westmanstown Golf Club   ★★

Clonsilla, Dublin 15, County Dublin
Nearest main town: Dublin

Secretary: Mr R. Monaghan   Tel: 01 820 5817
Professional: None.

Playing: Midweek: round £15.00; day £20.00. Weekend: round n/a; day n/a. Handicap certificate required.

Facilities: Bar: None. Food: None.

Comments: An 18-hole Eddie Hackett design, situated on the outskirts of Dublin, this parkland course features water on several holes and is maturing well ... Course improvements are ongoing, including the opening of a new 18th hole last year which features an approach shot over water to a well protected green.

Westport Golf Club   ★★★★

Carrowholly, Westport, County Mayo
Nearest main town: Westport

Secretary: Mr P. Smyth   Tel: 098 28262
(Manager)   Fax: 098 27217
Professional: Mr A. Mealia

Playing: Midweek: round £19.00; day n/a. Weekend: round £24.00; day n/a. Handicap certificate required.

Facilities: Bar: 10.30am–11pm. Food: Lunch and dinner from 10am–9pm. Bar snacks.

Comments: Excellent back nine ... Impressive locker room in friendly, welcoming clubhouse ... Views make it ... Don't give up, it gets better on the back nine ... Views of Croagh Patrick ... Long, tough, scenic inland course ... Course doesn't look great until the back nine ... 12th and 15th just great golf holes.

Index of Courses

Adare Manor 15
Ardee 39
Ardglass 72
Athenry 97
Athlone 97
Athy 39

Balbriggan 40
Balcarrick 40
Ballinasloe 98
Ballybofey & Stranorlar 72
Ballybunion (Cashen) 16
Ballybunion (Old) 11
Ballycastle 73
Ballyclare 73
Ballyheigue Castle 16
Ballykisteen 17
Ballyliffin (Glashedy) 69
Ballyliffin (Old) 74
Balmoral 74
Bandon 17
Bangor 75
Bantry Bay 17
Beaufort 18
Beaverstown 41
Beech Park 41
Black Bush 41
Blackwood 75
Bodenstown 42
Bright Castle 75
Bundoran 76

Cahir Park 18
Cairndhu 76
Carlow 42
Carrickfergus 77
Castle 43
Castle Barna 43
Castle Comer 43
Castle Hume 77
Castlebar 19
Castlerock 78
Castletroy 19

Castlewarden 44
Charlesland 44
Charleville 19
Cill Dara 45
City of Derry 78
Citywest 45
Clandeboye (Ava) 78
Clandeboye (Dufferin) 79
Clonmel 20
Clontarf 45
Coldwinters 46
Connemara 98
Cork 20
Corrstown 46
County Cavan 79
County Longford 47
County Louth 47
County Sligo 96
County Tipperary 21
Courtown 47
Craddockstown 99
Cruit Island 80

Deer Park 48
Delvin Castle 48
Dingle 21
Donabate 49
Donaghadee 80
Donegal 81
Dooks 22
Downpatrick 81
Dromoland Castle 22
Druid's Glen 49
Dun Laoghaire 50
Dundalk 50
Dungannon 81
Dungarvan 23
Dunmurry 82

Edenmore 82
Edmondstown 51
Ennis 23
Enniscorthy 51

Enniscrone 99

Faithlegg House 23
Fermoy 24
Forrest Little 51
Fortwilliam 83
Fota Island 24
Foyle International 83

Galway 99
Galway Bay 100
Glasson 52
Gort 100
Greenore 52
Gweedore 101

Harbour Point 25
Headfort 53
Hermitage 53
Hollywood Lakes 54
Holywood 84

Kenmare 25
Kilkea Castle 54
Kilkee 26
Kilkeel 84
Kilkenny 55
Killarney (Killeen) 26
Killarney (Mahoney's Point) 26
Killeen 55
Killeline 27
Killiney 56
Killorglin 27
Kinsale 28
Kirkistown Castle 84
Knockanally 56

Lahinch (Castle) 28
Lahinch (Old) 12
Lee Valley 28
Letterkenny 85
Limerick 29
Limerick County 29
Lisburn 85
Loughrea 101
Lucan 57

Lurgan 86
Luttrellstown Castle 57

Macroom 30
Mahee Island 86
Malahide 57
Mallow 30
Malone 87
Massereene 87
Milltown 58
Monkstown 30
Mount Juliet 36
Mount Temple 58
Mount Wolsley 59
Mountrath 59
Mullingar 59
Muskerry 31

Nairn & Portnoo 87
Newlands 101
North West 88
Nuremore 88

Old Conna 60
Old Head 13
Open Golf Centre 60
Oughterard 102

Parknasilla 31
Portadown 89
Portarlington 102
Portmarnock (Old) 37
Portmarnock Hotel and Golf Links 38
Portsalon 89
Portstewart 90
Powerscourt 61

Radisson Roe Park 90
Rathsallagh 61
Rockmount 90
Rosapenna 91
Roscommon 102
Rosecrea 32
Rosslare 62
Royal Belfast 91

Royal County Down 70
Royal Dublin 62
Royal Portrush (Dunluce) 71
Royal Portrush (Valley) 92
Rush 62

Scrabo 92
Seapoint 103
Shannon 32
Skerries 63
Slade Valley 63
Slieve Russell 93
Spa 93
St Helens Bay 64
St Margarets 64
Stackstown 103
Strandhill 104
Swords 64

Templepatrick 94
The Belvoir Park 94

The European Club 65
The Heath 65
The Island 66
The K Club 54
The Knock Club 95
Thurles 33
Tralee 14
Tramore 33
Tuam 104
Tullamore 66

Warrenpoint 95
Waterford 33
Waterford Castle 34
Waterville 34
West Waterford 35
Westmanstown 105
Westport 105
Wicklow 67
Woodbrook 67
Woodenbridge 67